The Western Frontier Library

(Complete list on page 118)

CATTLE-RAISING

ON THE PLAINS OF NORTH AMERICA

CATTLE-RAISING

OI

ON THE PLAINS

NORTH AMERICA

By Walter Baron von Richthofen

With an Introduction by EDWARD EVERETT DALE

Norman : University of Oklahoma Press

Library of Congress Catalog Card Number: 64-11320

New edition copyright 1964 by the University of Oklahoma Press, Publishing Division of the University. Composed and printed at Norman, Oklahoma, U.S.A., by the University of Oklahoma Press. First printing of the new edition.

DEDICATED TO THE CATTLEMEN OF COLORADO

INTRODUCTION

WALTER BARON VON RICHTHOFEN was an uncle of Manfried Baron von Richthofen, the celebrated flying ace of World War I. He was also related to Ferdinand von Richthofen, a distinguished geographer and explorer for whom Mount Richthofen, west of Rocky Mountain National Park, was named.

He was born in Kreisenitz, Silesia, in 1848, enlisted in the Prussian Army, and at the age of eighteen fought as a lieutenant in the so-called Seven Weeks' War with Austria. During this conflict he took part in at least two major battles. It is possible that after the end of the war he paid a brief visit to America. If so, he soon returned to Germany, for he was with the Prussian Army which invaded France during the Franco-Prussian War of 1870–71.

After the coming of peace he became a member of the bodyguard of the Emperor William I, but in the middle 1870's he sailed for the United States. He landed in New York and from there journeyed westward to Denver, where he lived for a considerable time before returning to Europe.

Apparently he liked Colorado very much for early in January he was married in London to Jane Oakley, a wealthy English girl, and immediately took his bride to Denver after a brief stop in Chicago. In Denver he purchased an attractive cottage, where he and his wife lived for some three years. Two daughters were born of this union, Margaretha, commonly called Daisy, and Charlotte.

Once settled in Denver, the Baron plunged with enthusiasm into the economic, civic, and social life of that fast-growing city. He purchased the Carlowitz Stock Farm, near Denver, and brought to it many thoroughbred Kentucky horses and colts. He trained these, engaged in trotting races, and held sales from time to time, but by the latter part of 1879 he had disposed of most of his racing stock. He also invested heavily in South Denver real estate and opened the Richthofen Subdivision in that part of the city. To bring prospective buyers to the addition he helped promote the Denver Circle Railroad. He then built a beer garden in South Denver called Sans Souci.

In 1882 he took the Baroness and their two baby daughters to visit his father in Prussia and then on to London for a visit with his wife's family. While there he asked Jane for a divorce. He returned alone to Denver and the divorce was soon granted. By its terms the mother retained her dowry and was given custody of the children. In 1885 she took them to Prussia as the Baron's father, of whom she was very fond, wanted his granddaughters educated in Germany.

Once back in Denver, the Baron resumed the gay bachelor life of the years before marriage. As a member of the Corkscrew Club, composed of well-born foreigners living in Denver, he promoted horse-racing events with all of the Old World trappings. Finding his South Denver project disappointing, he joined a company that was establishing a new town just east of Denver called Montclair, and became its guiding spirit. He arranged transportation to the new town, published maps, and sold lots. There he erected a two-story "milk house," with stalls on the ground floor for purebred dairy cows which he had imported, and porches above where tubercular patients might rest and drink rich milk from the animals stabled below.

He began the diligent wooing of Mrs. Louise Ferguson Woodall Davies, an attractive English-born divorcée, and they were married in November, 1887. Earlier in that year the Baron had begun the construction of a castle as their future home. It was built of gray stone with the Richthofen coat of arms on the north tower. He and the new Baroness lived in a hotel until it was completed and the grounds landscaped. They moved into it in November, 1888. Here they lived for about three years, the Baron devoting much time to the promotion of Montclair. He also built an art gallery to house paintings bought during his travels in Europe.

Early in 1891 the castle was offered for sale, but no buyer appeared so it was rented and the Baron and his wife left Denver to travel widely in Mexico and Europe. After a hunting trip to Alaska they settled in London, where the Baron formed the Anglo-Colorado Syndicate which invested heavily in Cripple Creek gold-mining ventures. He and the Baroness returned to Denver about 1895 with a grandiose scheme to establish a great resort with a hotel, bathhouse, and gambling casino. He formed the Colorado Carlsbad Company, in which Milwaukee businessmen were large investors. His plans seemed close to being realized when he was attacked by appendicitis. He died on May 8, 1898, after undergoing an operation.

Walter Baron von Richthofen had become an American citizen several years before his death. He left a lasting imprint upon Denver, where his castle still stands and where there are a street named Richthofen Place, two or three buildings which he erected, and the Richthofen fountain constructed after the Baron's death by contributions from his widow and friends.

The Baroness remained in Denver until her death in 1934. The two daughters were still living in Germany in 1960. Three of the Baron's grandsons were killed in World War II and one of his granddaughters, her husband, and three children committed suicide to avoid being sent to Siberia by the Russians.

Although *Cattle-Raising on the Plains of North America,* first published by D. Appleton and Company in 1885, was dedicated to the cattlemen of Colorado, the Baron himself was apparently never a ranchman. Diligent research has failed to reveal his name on the membership lists of any livestock association or a brand of his in any brand book. He owned dairy cattle, however, and race horses, and it is possible even if doubtful that he may have had a financial interest in some ranching enterprise or a few beef cattle on his stock farm.

Some of the material for the book was obtained by the Baron from friends in the Prairie Cattle Company, a huge syndicate established in Edinburgh about 1878 by the Scottish American Mortgage Company. The little volume is of great value because it not only gives excellent descriptions of the Great Plains area but lists the leading cattle companies of the early 1880's and has lengthy tables showing the increase to be expected from herds of breeding animals. While the author was highly optimistic about profits to be realized from ranching, he was no more so than most other writers of that period, including Clare S. Read and Albert Pell, both members of the British Parliament, who were sent to North America to study ranching and published their report in 1880. Ramon F. Adams, in his *The Rampaging Herd: A Bibliography of Books and Pamphlets on Men and Events in the Cattle Industry,* noted that *Cattle-Raising on the Plains of North America,* "with several other books of its kind, helped to create the cattle boom of the eighties."

EDWARD EVERETT DALE

Norman, Oklahoma
February 7, 1964

NOTE

HAVING LIVED IN COLORADO for many years, and being engaged in raising stock, I have become fully acquainted with the cattle business.

There being no book of which I have heard that treats the subject of cattle-raising in the West fully and systematically, I hope this publication may be of some use to those of my readers who contemplate embarking in this great industry.

WALTER BARON VON RICHTHOFEN

CONTENTS

Introduction by Edward Everett Dale   ix

Note by Walter Baron von Richthofen   xv

1—The Great American Desert   3

2—The Eldorado of the Day   6

3—The Cattle Herds of the West, and
   Comparative Statistics   9

4—Climate, Temperature, Vegetation, and Grass   12

5—Branding, Lassoing, Round-Up, Cowboys,
   Ranch, and Range   16

6—Herds and Breeds of Cattle—Labor on Ranch
   and Range   23

7—Cattle-Raising, a Legitimate and Safe
   Business   31

8—The Great Lands in the West—Prices and Future of the Same   44

9—Some of the Largest Herds   50

10—The Existing Cattle Companies Are Prosperous, and New Ones Are Constantly Being Formed   57

11—Choice Ranges for Breeding and Fattening Cattle—The Advantages from Having a Sufficient Number of Good Bulls   62

12—Profits in Cattle-Raising, and Fortunes Made Therein   70

13—Instances of Profits Realized   76

14—Profits to Accrue from a Proposed Plan   81

15—The Future of the Cattle Business in the West   99

16—Progress of the New West   107

CATTLE-RAISING

ON THE PLAINS OF NORTH AMERICA

1

THE GREAT AMERICAN DESERT

No DOUBT, some of my older readers will remember that when as boys they studied the geography of America, they were taught that all the land west of the Missouri River was barren and worthless, and that it would forever remain so. It was known that it was the abode of Indians and of wild beasts; that the buffalo roamed over its vast plains; and it commonly bore the name of "The Great American Desert."

Gradually the boundaries of this desert were moved farther and farther westward through the energy and labor of the so-called pioneers, who drove back the Indians, killed the comparatively few wild beasts, lessened the number of buffalo, plowed up the valleys and highlands, and built villages and towns. The new, fertile, and rich country thus developed was named "The New West."

After all this became known in the thickly populated Eastern states, thousands of emigrants and fortune-seekers turned their faces toward this new region. The more speculative engaged in mining, which has made many independent and some very wealthy, while the more careful soon recognized the fact that the raising of cattle would always be the most important, most profitable, and safest industry of the West. They remembered that on their journey westward they had seen, instead of a barren desert, continous plains covered with nutritious herbs and grasses, not utilized, but left to dry up and cure as winter came on, and to go to waste. They had seen herds of buffalo living on the plains without shelter, and getting fat. What was more natural than to conclude that, under such favorable circumstances, the business of raising cattle must be a profitable one?

Many of the latter class, who had a hundred dollars or so, bought small bunches of cattle and turned them loose on the open prairie, and they have since become independent, and in many cases rich, through the natural increase. Gradually their herds grew to hundreds and thousands of animals, and larger pastures became necessary. The most greedy of the large cattle-owners (called "Cattle Kings") then began to fear that they could not get enough grazing land for their enormous herds. They endeavored to perpetuate the belief among Eastern people that the plains were a desert. But the farmer-boys of the Eastern states, who were used to fourteen hours' work per day, were also desirous of obtaining a share of this strange Western country. They came here, plowed up the soil, took up the best valleys as homesteads, harvested larger crops, and demonstrated the fact that for agricultural purposes also this New West is indeed a true Eldorado, and that to call it a desert is to misname it.

To a certain extent the farmers interfered with the cattle business. They fenced up their farms and shut the cattle out from the water, and many a cattleman was obliged to seek new pasture grounds or to buy the farmer out. But as the area of the Far West contains 1,650,000 square miles, and as only a very small portion of this area—owing to its high altitude, the dryness of the atmosphere, and the light rainfall—can be used for agricultural purposes, cattlemen need have no fear of ever being crowded out by farmers.

Sixty years ago enthusiastic Americans boasted that their country had a desert equal to that of any other land; but now they are truly proud of being able to say that this former Great American Desert is the largest and richest grass and pasture region of the world, and that it will probably soon become the most important beef-producing country of the globe.

5

2

THE ELDORADO OF THE DAY

THOSE WHO HAVE TRAVELED through the West from the Missouri River to the Rocky Mountains, or still farther, are full of admiration for the natural resources of the country. Every river, every valley, every mountain, every pass, every hill, every plateau is useful for some purpose. The mountains hide immense treasures of precious minerals, and they are covered with forests. The river valleys, the mountain parks and passes, and the treeless prairie abound with grasses. The soil makes the plowman rich, and the other natural resources offer many opportunities for industrial undertakings. How is it that with such resources in the Far West, thousands of people still cling to their sandy, stony homes in Eastern America and Europe, where they can barely make a living, and where they receive but small returns for their investments?

6

During my last stay in Europe, I was surprised to find that so little was known of the resources and wealth of the West. Every one in Europe as well as in the Eastern states eats daily his beef, but very few seem to be aware that it is produced on the prairies of the "Far West" of North America. Although the immigration to the West is computed at half a million persons per annum, there is still room for millions. New discoveries, new improvements, new developments are daily occurring, and the West of last year is not that of this year. The only miracle of the nineteenth century is its growth. Less than fifteen years ago the first railroad was built through this country, while to-day the rails cross it in all directions. The rapidity of development and improvement is marvelous. We shall find ourselves at the end of the next twenty-five years living in a thickly populated state. Opportunities for wealth and high returns for one's money will have passed away, and industries, like the cattle business and land ownership, may become monopolies, as railroad and telegraph companies are now. Lands which can now be had at from two to ten dollars per acre will then be worth twenty-five to one hundred dollars per acre. All land situated in the valleys, and on higher places where irrigation can be had, will be occupied, producing large crops, and all the grazing lands will have owners.

In former years, before the fertility of the Western valleys and of those highlands where artifical irrigation can be effected was demonstrated, the cattle-owner was the sole possessor of the country, and was not obligated to be the owner of a single acre. Now it is different. He absolutely needs the running water, and is obliged to buy water front enough to control the grazing lands immediately behind, which are too high for the use of the agriculturist. Under the present demand for such pastures, prices are constantly increasing, and I would advise any one who contemplates emigrating from his overcrowded home, or any one who wishes for higher returns for his money, not to lose much time in obeying the world-renowned phrase of Horace Greeley, never regretted by any one who followed it: "Young man, go West!"

3

THE CATTLE HERDS OF THE WEST,
AND COMPARATIVE STATISTICS

My ASSERTION in the first chapter, that these Western prairies with their countless herds may become the meat-producing center of the world, is proved by the fact that they already occupy that position relative to the American nation, and that, according to statistics, the demand in London for American cattle is continually increasing. It is calculated that if in North America cattle-raising should suddenly cease, all present existing cattle would be eaten up within five years. Since 1860 thirty states and territories show a decrease, five are standing still, and only four show an increase of their stock in comparison with their population. According to statistics, the increase of population is much more rapid than that of stock. The proportion is $2\frac{3}{4}$ to $1\frac{1}{2}$ per cent. With this fact before us, we see that it is necessary to raise more stock, or the price of beef will rise continuously. I remember the time, not more than fifteen years ago, when I paid for beefsteak, cutlets, etc., less than ten cents a portion in Germany, while at my visit last year I paid as much as thirty-five cents. This shows a considerable increase in prices. Everybody knows how dear living has become in consequence of the constant rise in the price of beef.

This fact is very encouraging for cattle-breeders and herd-owners. For many years to come they need not have any fear of overproduction. The census of the United States shows a population of 50,000,000, with a yearly increase of 2¾ per cent. Cattle-raising does not keep pace with this rapid increase of population. The Eastern and Middle states show a rapid decrease of cattle. The land there is too dear to make the business of raising cattle profitable, and it pays the farmer better to turn all his attention to the cultivation of cereals and vegetables. Although he will always be obliged to raise a few cattle, he has already given up the idea of profitably raising herds; for he remembers that he must pay for his pasture from fifty to one hundred dollars per acre, and also must raise hay and fodder for his cattle, and that he has to compete with the herds raised out West on pastures formerly worth nothing and now perhaps only two or three dollars per acre, on which cattle thrive and fatten winter and summer without shelter. This great pasture region of North America has, as I said before, an area of 1,650,000 square miles, and is watered by hundreds of rivers and rivulets which head in the Rocky Mountains and furnish to the herds the purest, sweetest, and healthiest drinking water.

4

CLIMATE, TEMPERATURE, VEGETATION, AND GRASS

THE CLIMATE of these great pastures, as a whole, is excellent; it can not be compared with that in Europe and the East under the same latitude. Denver, for instance, lies farther south than Naples, and yet nearly every year in Denver one can enjoy a sleigh ride. Its summers are certainly not as hot and suffocating as those of Naples, and rarely can one omit a woolen blanket, or even two, in the summer nights. But it is a known fact that the farther west, the more moderate and warmer the climate gets; besides, the high altitude of this West partly accounts for the difference in temperature. All this immense district lies at an altitude of from 4,000 to 8,000 feet; the average temperature for the whole year is 50° to 55° Fahrenheit; the temperature in summer, between 45° and 75° to 90°; in winter, 25° to 32°. Of the 365 days of the year, 300 are clear with sunshine.

The snow line on Eastern mountains is 7,000 feet; on the Rocky Mountains, 12,000 feet. In consequence of this high altitude, the atmosphere is dry, the snow which falls, light; a trifle of wind blows the snow off, and the sun melts it quickly. This is fortunate for the herds, as the pasture is rarely snowed in for any length of time. Wet, cold winters, which in the Eastern states require the owners of cattle to house and shelter them, are not known here. The snow, even if it freezes, evaporates in consequence of the dry atmosphere.

I have read of a test of this statement: A moistened piece of cambric hung out on a very cold day on the prairie in the wind will freeze stiff at once, but very shortly afterward it will be again dry and soft. The ice in its fibers evaporates without melting, and so does the snow on the prairie. Vegetation in the East stops with 5,000 feet altitude, while here, even on the highest mountains, berries grow and evergreens blossom at an altitude of 11,000 feet. The rainfall averages eighteen inches per annum.

The pure, fresh mountain air, which is always and everywhere to be found, and the pure, fresh mountain water are natural preventives against ill-health and epidemics among cattle.

That cattle should find for the whole year more than enough food, even get fat on it, may be hard to understand; wherefore I will say a few words about the nature and growth of the grasses which are to be found on these prairies in abundance.

To name all the varieties of grasses and herbs of these prairies would take volumes. They grow in the early spring very rapidly. On the first of June they are in blossom. According to variety, they grow to a height of from six to twenty inches. At the end of June they are ripe, and the winds are the natural distributors of the seed for the next year's crop. The leaves and stems are dried by the end of July, and then the whole country looks yellow and brown like a ripe wheat-field; and thus the hay for the winter is prepared. As there is no moisture, this hay retains all its nutriment the whole winter. The little rainfall in the fall, and the light, dry snow in the winter, have not enough influence to hurt it. In the Eastern states it is claimed that early green grass has a weakening effect upon cattle, which is not the case here. This may be due to the fact that the young crop is well mixed with the other of last year.

Of all varieties of grass, the bunch grass, it is conceded, is the best for cattle. Another good variety is the grama. It grows, like all others, in the wet season of spring, ripens and cures when the dry season sets in, and

14

leaf and stem retain their nutritious qualities and offer excellent food the whole year through. Authorities claim that these grasses are equal to any of the cultivated grasses of the East. Governor McCook, of Colorado, says that the natural grasses of Colorado are even equal to the finest Hugarian grasses.

5

BRANDING, LASSOING, ROUND-UP, COWBOYS, RANCH, AND RANGE

TERMS USED in the cattle business are not generally known East and abroad, and I will therefore give their definition, as I shall have to use them repeatedly in the following chapters.

The owners of cattle in the Western stock-raising states are required by law to brand their stock with initials, figures, etc., chosen by themselves. The iron brands are attached to long handles, and pressed, when red-hot, upon one or the other side, or both sides, on especially selected parts of the animal, and thereby are written unmistakable and everlasting marks.

By law every brand must be registered in the office of the counties in which herds are expected to graze, and it is the duty of the recording clerk to see that a newcomer does not select an already registered brand. In

16

the change of ownership of cattle, the seller brands the animal with his "vend" brand, which is the proof for the buyer of his title, and the buyer puts his brand on in addition. The brand proves, therefore, the ownership or title to the animal.

Heretofore cattle have been caught by lassos and then branded. Of late, grown cattle have been driven into narrow shoots of varied lengths, and made to stand one behind the other, so close that they can hardly move, and the man through the openings between the timbers of the shoot impresses the brand.

Lassoing requires much practice, and is the great pleasure as well as the essential accomplishment of a good herder or cowboy.

Among cowboys are to be found the sons of the best families, who enjoy this romantic, healthy, and free life on the prairie.

Good opportunities to watch the skill of these cowboys are offered during round-ups, which is to the spectator a very interesting scene.

As the word shows, it is a rounding up and driving together of all the cattle within given limits to one selected spot. Naturally this work is performed on horseback, and every owner of cattle within the district, with his herders, takes part therein.

The purpose of a round-up is the following: As herds

17

spread over considerable territory, it would be a great sacrifice of time, money, and labor if single owners of herds had to hunt up singly their cattle in order to sell or to brand the same. For that reason the owners co-operate and drive all the cattle within their district together, make their bargains, brand their calves and steers, and complete the stock books of their herds, which owners are required by law to keep.

Between the middle of April and the end of June each year a general round-up is made, in which all herd-owners participate. Its principal purpose is the branding of the increase. In the months of September and October there are smaller round-ups, organized by those herd-owners who wish to collect fat steers for the market; but branding is also done.

Every Western state in which the industry of cattle-raising is important has its stock laws, the most important of which I will mention in an early chapter.

Every state government has subdivided its state into round-up districts, which vary in size between 100 and 150 square miles, according to the topography of the country. The governor of each state appoints a commission of three herd-owners in each district, called round-up commissioners, whose duty it is to see that the so-called round-up laws are executed; to make the programme for the general rounp-up; to fix the day of beginning, and subdivide their districts into smaller districts, averaging 10 to 12 square miles, which can be rounded up in a day, to publish in all papers the programme of the round-up, and appoint a captain as head of the practical execution of the same.

The captain is generally an experienced small herd-owner, who is thoroughly acquainted with the topography of his district, has an extensive knowledge of brands, and is familiar with the peculiarities of cattle.

From the beginning of the round-up he is the absolute commander.

On these days all the owners of cattle meet, attended with their herders, and well supplied with wagons, tents, blankets, provisions, and saddle horses.

The horses have the hardest work during the round-up, and are not expected to be used longer than half a day. Every herder needs to have at least from three to five horses in reserve.

The horses best adapted for cattle business are those raised on the plains. They are very hardy, between fourteen and fifteen hands high, large boned, and ugly looking. They cost between forty and fifty dollars apiece.

On the first day of a general round-up the camp is established. Twenty or thirty tents are pitched, and soon the smoke rises and the charms of a vivid camp life are offered to the eyes of the spectators. Wagons in profusion stand about, and hobbled horses graze around. The captain makes his general dispositions for round-up. The herd-owners divide the different duties of the work among their herders—some to go on the round-up, some to do branding, and others to cut out the beeves which are to be sold and drive them to the nearest railroad station or market. The buyers and sellers exchange their opinions regarding the interests and future of the business, and often conclude bargains.

The next morning early the work begins. The captain collects his herders, and gives them their instructions where to ride, where to find the cattle, and where to drive them.

This spot, where all cattle within the day's district are to be driven together, has been previously selected by the captain. It is generally a place, not necessarily in the center of the district, where a large herd of cattle can easily be controlled, and where there is grass and water enough for a large number of animals for several days.

After the herders have received their general instructions, they gallop off right and left, while the owners, buyers, and ever-present spectators move toward the place where the large herd will be rounded up.

In a few hours one can note scattered groups of cattle approaching, followed by larger masses, until the herders themselves bring up, with yell and halloo, the refractory and more stubborn animals. Toward noon from two to five thousand head of cattle are collected. It is by no means an easy task to quiet so large a herd. It generally takes an hour or two for the different groups of strange cattle to learn to tolerate each other's presence, and to establish quiet among the steers, many of which make frequent attempts to break through the chain of herders, which is kept up around the herd day and night, like a cordon of sentries. At last one can see how the larger and stronger steers, seeking the center of the herd, resign themselves to their fate, and how the careful mother-cow keeps her calf on the outside, away from the danger of being trampled down or hurt by its older and untamed brothers and cousins.

Now begins the work of branding the calves.

The cowboy rides into the herd, cuts out a cow with an unbranded calf, throws his well-directed lasso, catches and jerks the calf to the ground, which another herder quickly brands and releases from the lasso; and then they seek out another victim. Some of the herd-owners collect all their cows and calves in a bunch, drive them to their home ranches, and do the branding there after the general round-up is over.

If sales of grown cattle are made, the buyer brands his purchases on the spot, lassoing them as above described, which is very hard work. If a great number are to be branded, branding-pens must be constructed, or the cattle driven to the home ranch. As stated before, owners of herds can now count their cattle.

As evening approaches it is very difficult to keep a herd together, but at night the cattle generally lie down and sleep. The work is resumed the next day, and continued from day to day until all the calves or grown cattle are branded and all steers and barren cows intended for market are cut out and collected, when the rest of the herd are allowed to go free. These proceedings often occupy several days. The camp then breaks up and moves to another part of the district, where the same work is repeated, and so on until the whole district has been gone over.

Only one who has seen a round-up of large herds can have an idea of the wealth which is to be found on the vast prairies and among the valleys and mountains of the West.

HERDS AND BREEDS OF CATTLE—
LABOR ON RANCH AND RANGE

THE ORIGINAL STOCK of cattle in the West came from Texas. Hundreds of thousands of these cattle are driven yearly from that state into the more northern districts. The driving and selling of cattle from Texas is a business by itself. Nearly every one has, I presume, seen a Texas steer, with its long horns, long legs, and large but rather thin body. Their average weight when fat is about one thousand pounds. They are the cheapest in the market, although their price has nearly doubled in the last ten years. From this breed others have been reared, three-quarters Texas, half Texas, and so forth, until now one speaks only of the American breed. All these different grades have been crossed with Durham, Hereford, and other blooded bulls imported from the East.

The prices of the different grades depend on their

quality and the time and place where bought. For the last few years it has been the aim of herd-owners to improve the blood of their herds, thereby obtaining higher prices and enabling them to compete in weight and taste of meat with the Danish, Russian, and Dutch cattle, their rivals in the London market, where shipload after shipload of American Western-raised cattle are constantly arriving.

That the American beef trade in England has increased and is still increasing is a fact, in proof of which I quote the following, taken from a report by J. Berger, Spencer & Co., of London and Manchester, England, issued August 15, 1883: "The formation in England and Scotland of large companies for the purchase of ranches in Western America is reported steadily on the increase. Reports as to large dividends by many Scotch companies are favorable, some being as high as 30 per cent." This firm declared that any properly managed cattle ranch is sure to pay well. Great Britain imported from the United States and Canada, during the seven months ending July 31, 1882, 45,269 beef-cattle, valued at $5,306,965.00, and for the same period in 1883, 97,721 head, valued at $11,082,040.00, or $113.40 per head.

We are sorry that this circular fails to give the importation of fresh (otherwise called "dead") meat from the United States. It states, however, that England received from all countries during the first seven months of 1882 dead meat valued at $3,745,545.00, and for the corresponding period of 1883 the valuation was $6,517,-115.00, an increase of nearly $3,000,000.00. This increase we regard as a mere trifle when we take into consideration the vast proportions which the future trade in dead and living meats is destined to reach. Ere many years Texas alone will furnish to Europe more meat than is now received in Great Britain from all foreign ports.

Notwithstanding the steady advance in price, Texas ranches and cattle are at present far below their real worth. The reason for the increased price of cattle during the last five or six years, and the prospect of a continued rise, lies mainly in the increasing demand for beef in America as well as in foreign countries. The present prices for medium-grade Western stock are as follows:

Cows $27 to $32

Two-year-old heifers $20 to $25

Yearlings $16 to $20

Calves $12 to $14

Four-year-old steers $40 to $45

Three-year-old steers $30 to $35

Two-year-old steers $25 to $30

Yearling steers $16 to $20

Graded Durham or Hereford cows $50 to $60

Graded Durham or Hereford bulls $50 to $100
Full-blooded bulls $200 to $500

The differences in prices are due to quality and to the time and place of purchase. The above table represents the prices paid for cattle when bought for stock purposes, while in the beef market the price is determined by the weight of the animal. At present the prices are three cents per pound for Texas and four to five cents per pound for American beef.

Between the domestic or stable-reared cattle of the Eastern states and of Europe and those reared on the Western prairies there exists a great difference. Although the latter cannot strictly be called wild, yet they have peculiarities in their nature common to the buffalo. For instance, they run away if they see somebody on foot. A cow will often defend her calf when it is caught by the lasso; they move about in families, grazing and herding together, and the attachment of a cow to her calf, and vice versa, is much greater than that of the domestic animal. Here and there one can watch groups of families where the offspring of three or four generations have never been separated. The mother of all always retains her authority, and even punishes her children and grandchildren, though they may be much larger than herself; but in the defense of families the female yields precedence to the male.

26

The prairie calf is much stronger than the domestic one, and is altogether a more healthy and rapidly developing animal. And why not? It receives as food all of its mother's milk without any stint, and is not, like its cousins in Eastern stables, deprived thereof and half starved.

About noon herds move toward their watering places, where they remain for two or three hours, and then, like buffalo, march back in single file to their favorite pasture grounds. In summer they seldom graze farther than five or six miles from water, while in winter they spread over more territory, often remaining two or three days without water, and even eating snow for drink. During a heavy snow storm groups and families gather together into small herds, and, with their back to the storm, shelter one another. Long-continued snow storms drive such herds from their home pastures into other regions; but when the storm clears they generally return to their haunts. In northern climates, where snow storms are more frequent, cattle die from hunger only when they are so driven for shelter in large numbers to a place with natural barriers which stop them, and where they soon consume all the grass; but this very seldom happens. As a rule, cattle cling with instinctive love to the pastures which they have once occupied.

The duties of the herders may now be mentioned.

From April to June, during the general round-up, herders have the hardest work of the year. From July to the end of August the herder, always on horseback, hunts in neighboring pastures for strayed cattle, drives them back to their own pastures, and brands such young calves as he may find. The finding of lost cattle is not as difficult as may at first appear, for the cattlemen are always on good terms with one another. When a herder arrives at a camp inquiring after lost stock, he invariably receives all information from willing friends and offers of assistance. Herders when on the hunt for lost cattle are never allowed to pay for their lodgings overnight, and, should one of their horses be tired out or lame, they always are offered another without charge.

September and October are the months for private round-ups for the purpose of collecting beef for the market, and for branding any calves that may have escaped. Unbranded calves, if found with their mothers, even though they may not belong to the parties interested in these fall round-ups, are branded for their real owners, and a registry kept and forwarded to those interested. This latter work, which is not paid for, but is a matter of honor, proves how herd-owners help one another.

The labor in November and December is much the same as in midsummer, only perhaps more with the view of finding lost fat-beef cattle for market. Between January and April there is very little work to be done. During that time the cattle get rest and are not molested by being constantly driven. According to the resolutions of the association of cattle-growers, no calf may be branded during this time. All that the herders are then expected to do is to keep a general supervision of the stock, and after snow storms to drive lost stock back to their ranges. During the whole year the herders have many different jobs to perform on their home ranches, such as cooking, cutting wood, hay-making, etc.

The following statement shows how many herders are necessary for the management of a herd of five thousand head, and the cost of their pay and sustenance:

A good foreman engaged by the year is indispensable. His salary may be from $60 to $70 per month, with free lodging and board, valued at about $20 per month. From the first of April to the first of July seven herders are necessary, each at a salary of $35 per month and board. From the first of July to the first of December only five herders are needed, and from that time until the first of April the foreman with one herder can do all the work. The wages for the whole year would amount to $2,580, and board would cost $1,120. Total $3,700 per annum. The estimate of the cost of board may be too high;

$3,500 per annum would probably be ample. From this we see that the cost of labor in herding five thousand head is seventy cents per head per annum. To keep one thousand head more would cost but a trifle addition.

The equipment for every herder consists of from three to five ponies, a first-class Mexican saddle, lasso, etc. I have already described the kind of horses which are used. They are never fed with grain, but have to find their own food like the cattle. Their only training is in accustoming them to the saddle and the throwing of the lasso, in which they play the most important part. In former years owners of small bunches of cattle hired the herding of their stock for a percentage of the increase, or paid one dollar per head per annum. This is seldom done now, and only in cases where owners can not devote their whole time and attention to their cattle.

7

CATTLE-RAISING,
A LEGITIMATE AND SAFE BUSINESS

MANY WHO HAVE NOT GIVEN much thought to this business will not understand how a business in which the owner sees his property only once or twice a year can possibly be called a safe one. Nevertheless, it is pronounced by all who are acquainted with it as not only safe as any other branch of industry, but perhaps more so. There are no risks beyond losses arising from natural causes, which can be calculated down to a percentage per annum, and none arising from speculation. The stock, once bought, will remain and increase. In every business, whether the mercantile, manufacturing, or professional, every one engaged therein counts on losses during a year's business. Therefore it is not to be wondered at that also in the cattle business there are losses, and it is by reason of the amount or variety of losses that any business is deemed safe or risky. I will in this chapter make my readers acquainted with the various losses, and causes thereof, occuring in cattle-raising in the West, and the means by which these losses have been, by long experience and good protective laws, reduced to an average of 2 to 3 per cent per annum of the stock, which is far less than 3 per cent of the money value of the herd.

Losses arise from the following causes:

1. Sickness among cattle.
2. Killing of cattle by railroads.
3. Extreme cold with lasting snow.
4. Straying of cattle into other districts.
5. Theft of cattle and calves.

The last-mentioned cause for losses gave in the early years of cattle-raising the largest percentage; but now it is, in consequence of well-regulated protective laws and of co-operation of all stockmen, reduced to a minimum: and it may be said right here that there is more thieving going on in the center of a metropolis, which is guarded day and night by well-trained policemen and watchmen, than on the desolate prairies.

Sickness from natural causes, and death arising from it, are certainly among the Western cattle herds just the same as in Eastern or European ones; but contagious epidemics, which sweep away the cattle by the hundreds in the East and Europe, have never been known among

32

Western herds. Nature itself here, the climate and altitude, as already described, the healthy natural food they live on, and the pure, fresh water they drink, preclude epidemic diseases.

Railroads now cross the Western pasture lands everywhere from north to south, east to west, and it seems to be a pleasure for cattle to stand or lie on the tracks. Although every train uses precautions to prevent accidents, still not unfrequently it happens that some of the more stubborn cattle are thrown from the track by the cow-catcher in the front of the locomotive, and killed or crippled.

In early days the owners of so-killed cattle never perhaps heard of the accident, and attributed simply the loss of their cattle to other causes; but wise protective stock-laws now make railroad companies responsible therefor. They have to pay for the loss, the amounts thereof we will mention later. The owner sustains loss from this cause only in case a cow is killed leaving an unbranded calf, which necessarily dies unless it finds another cow to act as mother.

Such motherless, unbranded calves, called mavericks, become by law, when the ownership cannot be proved, the property of the cattle-growers' association of the district in which the calf is found.

In former years these mavericks were the property

of the person who found them first, he having the privilege of putting his brand on them. In most cases the cowboys benefited thereby, which led them by and by to neglect their owners' herds in order to accumulate in this manner herds for themselves.

This has been stopped by the so-called maverick laws. Mavericks, the law says, are to be caught on the first day of every round-up, branded, and sold to the highest bidder; every round-up district must have its own maverick brand, and, before selling, has to brand every maverick and keep a record of the same. The money accruing from such sales is used by the round-up district to defray the salary of the captain of the round-up, and other expenses, such as publishing its programme, etc. The private branding of mavericks is punished as theft.

In the more northerly situated cattle territory, Wyoming and Montana, heavy snowfalls are sometimes followed by freezing weather. The prairie is covered then by a crust of ice, and the cattle are not able to get enough food. In such extreme cases the poor, lean cattle, which are too weak to endure several days' fasting, die of hunger. This happens very seldom, as such storms are not frequent in this climate.

As I mentioned in a former chapter, long-continued, heavy snow storms will drive herds into other districts, and although most of the cattle will return to their home pasture as soon as the weather clears, yet some may stray away, and occasionally the owner, after hunting around in vain, may conclude an animal has died or been killed. Even then the animal is not necessarily lost, for I have known cattle to be found after a lapse of three years, and not only the original cattle, but also their increase.

Since stock-growers' associations are working hand in hand for their common interests, there is not much fear of losing a hoof from this cause.

In the early days of the business, losses caused by theft occurred somewhat frequently. It was a new industry, and profits were so large that if a man lost a head occasionally, which he even knew to have been stolen, he did not care much about it, and put himself to no expense to prosecute the thief.

If thefts became too frequent, he took the law in his own hands, and, if he caught the thief, he simply shot him, or called his neighbors together and hanged him on the first tree, as a warning to others.

Gradually the cattle-owners recognized the necessity of close co-operation. Cattle-growers' associations were formed in each state, and district associations in respective round-up districts. Nearly all of the herd-owners joined them for the purpose of advancing the general interests of cattle-raising, of studying means for the protection of their common property, and of prosecuting trespassers.

In union lies strength, as was manifested in this case, since the resolutions adopted by the associations became state law through the influence of the members.

As there is among stockmen no competition, save that every one tries to increase his property and to improve the breed of his cattle, there is no business jealousy, and all work hand in hand for their common interests and for the interest of each individual.

The most important stock-laws are the following:

1. Every railroad or railway corporation operating any line of railroad or any branch thereof is obliged to keep at one station in each county through which it runs a register-book open to the inspection of any one, in which the company must record every head of stock killed or crippled, with exact description of the same, color, age, brand, sex, etc., within fifteen days after the accident.

2. Every railroad company that kills or cripples stock shall be liable to the owner of such animals for the damages sustained by the owner according to the schedule prices made by the state from time to time.

3. Killed animals belong to the railroad companies, which may sell the same, but must keep the hide for a

period of thirty days for inspection.

4. All brands shall be recorded in the county where the owner resides, and it is the duty of the recorder to see that the same brand is not recorded twice.

5. All young stock found running at large without a mother, and upon which there is no brand, shall be deemed mavericks, and may be taken in charge by the captain or foreman of the legal round-up, and sold on the first day of its meeting to the highest bidder. The proceeds arising from the sales shall be paid into the treasury of the association of the district in which such maverick has been taken up.

6. Every person, before he shall set up and carry on the trade or business of a butcher or slaughterer of horned cattle in the state, shall file a bond with the clerk of the county in which he desires to carry on the business, in a sum not less than one thousand nor more than five thousand dollars, conditioned that he shall keep a true and faithful record, in a book kept for the purpose, of all cattle purchased or slaughtered by him, with the description of the animal, including marks, brands, age, weight, and from whom purchased and the date thereof, and shall keep the hide and horns of such animal free to the inspection of all persons for the period of thirty days after it is slaughtered.

7. The governor shall appoint three commissioners

for each district, to be known as Round-up Commissioners, who shall be actual owners of cattle upon the range within the district for which they are appointed. Said commissioners arrange the programme for the actual spring round-up, fix its date, appoint the captain, and generally watch over the execution of all round-up laws.

8. The governor shall appoint each year five commissioners from different sections of the state, to be known as the Board of Inspection Commissioners. No person who is not the actual owner of cattle running on such section shall be eligible to serve on said board. Each commissioner shall take and subscribe to an oath conditioned for the faithful performance of his duties as commissioner.

9. It shall be the duty of said board to employ competent cattle inspectors and to distribute them at points, either within or without the boundaries of the state, as will in their judgment most effectually prevent the illegal slaughtering or shipping of cattle. They shall also furnish each inspector with a list of all brands sent to them for that purpose and owned by residents of the state. All inspectors, while thus employed, shall be subject to such reasonable rules and requirements as the board may prescribe, and shall be subject to dismissal by the board at any time. Inspectors receive the sum of one hundred dollars per month during their time of actual service.

The duty of these inspectors is similar to that of private or secret detectives. They have free fare on all railroads; they inspect every slaughter house, butcher-shop, and every transportation line.

This institution of inspection has been very efficient in stopping the thefts of cattle. Besides their salaries, the inspectors can earn high rewards, offered by the cattle-growers' association, for the detection of thefts and the capture of the thieves. These rewards are also offered to every citizen.

In order to show that all precautions are taken and means used to prevent depredations on stock, I quote some of the resolutions of the Colorado Cattle-Growers' Association, adopted in January, 1881:

WHEREAS, it has been the custom of a goodly number of prominent cattlemen to violate the existing stock laws as regards mavericks; by doing so, inducing cowboys to start maverick brands, etc., etc. Therefore we, as cattle-owners of Colorado, do bind ourselves upon honor and justice toward our fellow-cattlemen, etc., etc.

1. We hereby agree that our first duty lies in recommending to the Governor for appointment as round-up commissioners such men as we can repose special confidence in.

2. That we will see that the round-up commissioners for our respective districts fully carry out the provisions of our round-up and maverick laws; and, in addition,

that it shall be their duty to lay out a programme for a second hunt in their several districts, and make the time and programme known to the general round-up ten days prior to abandoning the same; and, further, that whenever it shall come to their knowledge that any person or persons are engaged in rounding-up cattle in an unauthorized manner, it shall be their duty to employ inspectors and attorneys and take such action as will stop such unauthorized handling of cattle.

3. That upon the rounding-up of cattle it shall be the duty of the captains of a round-up to first cut out all mavericks prior to any other work or cutting out; and that they shall be sold upon the same day of such cutting out, as provided by law; and, further, that the same shall be branded with the maverick brand that may be adopted for the district in which they are sold. This procedure shall apply to the second round-up in the same manner as to the general hunt.

4. That we will in no case brand a motherless calf, or maverick, or allow it to be done, or in any way convert any animal not strictly our own to our benefit; and we further pledge ourselves that, after the general hunts are over, in our minor or beef hunts, we will place the maverick brand adopted for our respective districts upon all motherless or maverick cattle, and keep a descriptive list of the same.

5. We further agree to fully carry out the programme

of round-ups as laid out by the round-up commissioners of our several districts; and, further, that we will in no event brand calves, or cause to be branded, after the first day of January of each year and prior to the stipulated time of general round-up of cattle by the commissioner.

6. We further agree that we will, after the first day of September of each year, brand all unbranded calves with owner's brand that may be found belonging to any one who may be a party to this contract, and that we will keep, or cause to be kept, a true and correct list of such calves branded. This list must be returned to the office of the district association prior to the 15th of December, and forwarded to the Secretary of the State Association prior to the first of January.

7. That any employé violating any of the provisions of this agreement shall be discharged from our employ, and that in no event will he receive employment at the hands of others who are parties to this contract.

Of further interest may be the report of Wetzell & Wilson, issued January, 1882:

Twelve years ago a small number of cattlemen assembled to form an association for mutual benefit and protection. Cattle-raising was in its infancy, but co-operation was already necessary.

From that day on the Colorado Cattle-Growers' Association has grown in strength and importance till it has become the most important factor in the control and management of this great industry. Step by step, year after year, we have already advanced in learning how to take care of our herds and in making and improving laws for their protection of which we may be proud.

Take, for instance, our system of inspection. There are many who will remember how we were constantly exposed to the thieving, etc.; how we had ourselves to watch day and night slaughter-houses, etc. Since then we have such a safe law of inspection that any cattle-owner, no matter where he resides, has but to send a certified copy of his brand to the Secretary of the State Inspection Commission, and it will be put in the hands of inspectors in Omaha, Kansas City, Denver, and all other important places where cattle are shipped or slaughtered, and any cattle coming in such places must be identified, or the persons who have them are arrested and the cattle returned to the owner.

During the month of September, 1881, a car-load of cattle was stolen from Jefferson County and shipped to Kansas City, six hundred miles. Our inspector in Kansas City discovered that there was something wrong. They bore brands he did not know, and the party could not give satisfactory explanations. After diligent search, the inspectors found that the cattle were stolen in Jefferson County. The offender was arrested, and served his sentence in Cañon City.

Round-ups, formerly in the hands of county commissioners, are now controlled by the Governor of the State, the whole State being laid out in round-up districts. We have laws concerning prairie-fires, concerning cattle killed by railroads, and all matters pertaining to cattle intrests, which are as near perfect as they can be.

8

THE GREAT LANDS IN THE WEST—
PRICES AND FUTURE OF THE SAME

SOME OF MY READERS may not know by what means landed property can be obtained in the United States. The United States is the original owner of the public lands in the West, and gives to the first individual applying therefor a patent for the same. To this general rule there are a few exceptions.

In the year 1845, Texas, then a state of Mexico, revolted against its general government and became an independent republic. This led, in 1846, to the Mexican-American War, and the United States received as war indemnity the Mexican domain, which now forms the states and territories of Colorado, California, New Mexico, and Arizona.

Texas joined by its own will the North American Republic, but reserved its rights in and ownership of its lands. Being in need of money, it issued land-script, by which millions of acres of land are placed in pledge.

The value of this land-script has fluctuated ever since, and many speculators came into possession of large tracts of land which did not cost them more than perhaps twenty or thirty cents per acre.

For the construction of the State Capitol, which is to cost $2,000,000, Texas sold 3,000,000 acres of public domain. This area will soon be fenced by the purchasers and used as a cattle range.

Pasture land at the present time is worth in Texas from one to three dollars per acre, according to quality and location.

The former Spanish and later Mexican governments of old Mexico were very lavish, and gave large tracts of land to statesmen, warriors, and other officals who had proved loyal or had rendered valuable services.

These grants are of different sizes, varying from 10,000 to 1,000,000 acres or more.

The boundaries of these grants, some of which were given as far back as the year 1700, are often very vaguely described, and it became necessary to have all the grants resurveyed by the government of the United States. When such surveys are approved by the surveyor-general of the proper territory, the title is as valid as if the United States had issued the patent.

In former days these large tracts of land had hardly any value, but, since the advent of Americans in New Mexico and the introduction of railroads, they have become very desirable properties as sheep and cattle ranges. The prices vary, according to location, quality and quantity, from one to three dollars per acre.

One can not buy large, continuous tracts of land directly from the United States. Every citizen has the right to take up 160 acres, wherever he chooses, as a homestead, but he must live on the same land for five consecutive years, after which time the government issues to him a patent free of charge.

Another privilege of every citizen is to pre-empt another 160 acres upon condition that he makes for three years certain improvements and then pays $1.25 an acre for the same. Both the homestead and pre-emption right the citizen can exercise once only in his life. Without paying for the land, and without improvement or homestead conditions, the soldier has a claim once in his life for 160 acres.

The soldiers' rights were sold by the thousands to land speculators after the close of the Mexican War.

The only donations of large tracts of land by the government were made to railroads, which opened up new districts, and from these latter companies large tracts may be bought; but even they are not continuous, as it is the practice of the United States to reserve every alternate section.

In the early days of cattle-raising it was not necessary for the owners of herds to have the titles to any land; all they required was to find a good pasture with running water, which they simply occupied with their cattle.

After the fact was demonstrated that the valleys with running streams were very productive, farmers soon took the land, fenced it, and obliged the cattle-owners in some places to leave the country, or to buy them out, and soon all desirable water fronts were owned by one or the other. When the irrigation of the higher lands became more general the herd-owners were obliged to buy still more land, in order that their cattle might not be fenced out and prevented from coming to the water.

In fact, in consequence of the increasing settlement by farmers, the cattle-owner is now obliged to own a great portion of the pasture, at least the water front, with enough country back of it to control the pasture in the rear of that, which is useless for the farmer. As a consequence, land grants, when large enough, are now in favor.

This demand for pasture lands increases in value, and I should not be surprised if, in less than twenty years, an acre of pasture land should cost nearly as much as agricultural land. The latter varies now from ten to thirty dollars an acre, while pasture land can yet be bought at from two to four dollars.

The rise of the pasture value is a good sign.

The fact that the herd-owner is willing to pay a good price for his land furnishes the best proof that cattle-raising is flourishing and very profitable.

The constantly increasing interest which Eastern and European capitalists take in the industry of cattle-raising brings pasture grounds at the present time into great demand; the prices are constantly increasing, and the opportunity of buying at present prices will soon be as rare as is to-day the chance of buying at prices of five years ago.

The ownership of pasture lands is just as much needed as the money to buy stock with—indeed, a man controlling large pasture lands has no trouble in getting capital enough to stock it.

Since the ranges have become larger, they are also more and more improved. Better and more comfortable houses take the place of the old log-cabins; substantial corrals, branding-pens, and sheds are built; the best portions are fenced up for hay-making, and others are fenced in as special pastures for weak, sickly, and better-bred animals; and the owner finds that by improving his land he also increases its value.

He is also now enabled to raise his own blooded bulls, which he was formerly obliged to import at high expense from Eastern states; such bulls, born here, and consequently acclimated, will do more service, and thus bring more money into the owner's pockets.

9

SOME OF THE LARGEST HERDS

STATISTICS WILL BEST SHOW the magnitude of the cattle business in the West and South.

Texas alone is credited with having 40,000,000 head of cattle running on its prairies, although hundreds of thousands are driven yearly north to replenish the herds of the other states.

The Northwestern Texas Cattle-Raising Association has 223 members, who own from 1,000 to 60,000 cattle, and represent a total of 1,400,000 head. Several of them can boast of herds of 40,000 to 60,000 head, and there are 14 members who own 20,000 head each.

Among the first from the North to embark in the cattle business in Texas were the Harrold brothers, of Illinois, who started, in 1875, in Green *(sic)* and Tom Green counties. They invested $48,000 in 4,300 head of cattle. To-day they are owners of 60,000 head, worth at least $1,500,000.

During 1882 they sold 10,000 head, and this year will brand more than 15,000 calves. For the last six years they have been improving their herd by crossing with Shorthorns and Herefords.

One of the largest herds is that of Charles Goodnight. He began, four years ago, buying land at the head of Red River—270,000 acres—at thirty-five cents per acre. In the meantime the price of land has advanced to one and two dollars an acre; but he is still buying more, and now controls 700,000 acres.

To enclose his landed possession, 250 miles of fence is required. He has a herd of 40,000 head. This is not the largest in the state, but it is the finest, having been carefully graded up. The superiority of the herd is generally conceded. Recently he obtained for 200 yearlings $20 per head, while the average price of Texas yearlings is only $15. He branded last year 10,000 calves.

The Matador Cattle Company's ranch is situated in Motley and Cottle counties, on Peace River. This property includes 100,000 acres of land, and was recently sold to a company of Scotch capitalists for $1,250,000.

The Worsham Cattle Company, in Wilbarger and Hardeman counties, have 35,000 head.

The Western Land and Cattle Company of London

was organized in 1882, with capital stock of £300,000. They have 30,000 head, mostly half-breeds, in the Panhandle and on the borders of New Mexico. James A. Forbes, of London, is managing director in America.

The Chicago and Texas Cattle Company, a recent organization, has 12,000 to 13,000 head on the Colorado and North Concho rivers. The herd costs $215,000.

Nelson Mordant recently bought 124,000 acres in Tom Green and Andrew counties, which he intends to fence and stock up with cattle.

Adjoining this property, John R. Honie has 51,200 acres.

The Chicago Syndicate, composed of J. V. Farwell, C. B. Farwell, Abner Taylor, and Colonel Babcock, which had the contract of building the State Capitol at Austin, received for this outlay 3,000,000 acres of choice land. The cost of this structure was $2,000,000. It is the intention to stock this immense property with cattle.

Colonel King, of Texas, has sold his cattle and range near San Antonio, for $4,000,000, to an English syndicate, and it is now the largest range in the world.

The Prairie Cattle Company's property lies in three divisions. The first, the Arkansas or Northern Division, extends from the Arkansas River on the north to the state line of Colorado and New Mexico on the south, a distance of seventy miles, and from a line drawn north and south at a distance of ten miles west of the town of La Junta, on the Atchison, Topeka, and Santa Fe Railroad, it extends a distance of fifty miles eastward, embracing a territory of 3,500 square miles, or 2,240,000 acres. On this princely range there are 53,982 cattle. To manage this herd, 300 horses are used by the rancheros. Value of the land, $163, 992; of cattle $1,705,000; total $1,791, 492.

The second, Cimarron, or Central Division, extends from the state line of Colorado and New Mexico on the north to the southern line of Mora County, New Mexico, on the south, a distance of eighty-four miles, and from a line drawn north and south, of Sierra Grande, on the west, to the Texas state line on the east, a distance of forty-eight miles, embracing an area of 4,032 square miles, or 2,580,480 acres. Lands in this division are estimated to be worth $235,545; the number of cattle is 57,799, and their value $1,444,975. The value of the whole property is $1,753,920. In the management, 500 horses are used. General headquarters are located here, and the greater part of the Southern rounding-up is managed from this range. A telephone line of 150 miles connects the general headquarters with those of the Northern Division.

The Canadian or Southern Division of the company's

property is situated on the Canadian River, in the counties of Potter and Oldham. In the Panhandle of Texas the longest cross-lines are twenty-five and sixteen miles, respectively, and the area is 400 square miles, 256,000 acres. The land is not so good as in the other divisions. The price paid for the land was sixty cents per acre, while the value of the 29,803 cattle is $715,272, and of the 200 horses $8,000. The whole property is worth $771,072. The herds are carefully graded with Durham, Shorthorn, and Hereford blood. The increase has been very large. The grand total value of the three ranges, cattle, and improvements is placed at $4,316,484.[1]

The Prairie Cattle Company began three years ago with 104,000 head of cattle. This number has in two years increased to 139,000, while in the meantime the company has drawn from the beef sufficient to pay all expenses and £10,000 in 1881, and in 1882, £50,000 of profit. The number of calves branded in 1882 was about 26,000.

The Cimarron Cattle Company in New Mexico, on the Cimarron River, has about 12,000 acres of water

[1]Even though most of the figures in the foregoing three paragraphs do not total properly, they are reprinted here exactly as they appeared in the original edition of *Cattle-Raising on the Plains of North America*. Without access to the old records of the Prairie Cattle Company, it would not now be possible to correct these figures.—*The Publisher*.

frontage, with sufficient control of range to herd their 20,000 head of cattle.

The Red River Cattle Company in New Mexico owns the Noland Grant, with 150,000 acres of fine land of which 100,000 are fenced. This company has 6,000 head of cattle, and will sell after this year yearly 2,000 head of steers.

The American Cattle Company of Scotland operates in western Nebraska, The range consists of 1,500 square miles on both sides of the Niobrara River, which the company bought in 1881, with 23,000 head of cattle.

The Maxwell Cattle Company, a new organization, has leased the Maxwell Grant in New Mexico, with 1,400,000 acres, for thirty-eight years, and the capital stock issued is £200,00. This grant is capable of sustaining 80,000 head of cattle; just now 16,000 head are on it.

The Powder River Cattle Company of Wyoming has a capital stock of £300,000, and includes among its directors the Duke of Manchester, William Tipping, Lord Henry Neville, Ernest Berkel Denison, and Andrew Whitton. The landed property is valued at $258,-000.

The largest herd-owner of Wyoming was Mr. A. H. Swan, who sold recently to a new Scotch syndicate his

67,000 head of cattle for $2,500,000, and is now managing the business.

The Marquis de Mores, the French cattle king on the Little Missouri River in Montana, is constructing buildings necessary for the purpose of killing and dressing beef on this range, and his intention is to kill eighty beeves, or two car loads, per day. A company has been organized in St. Paul, under the name of the Northern Pacific Refrigerator Car Company, with a capital of $200,000. It has a contract for ten years with the Northern Pacific Railroad, and will transport the meat from this place.

Besides the cattle interest of the Marquis de Mores at that point, a herd of 14,000 Texas cattle and Colorado steers, with some Herefords, will be driven to that locality from Colorado, W. A. Towers, of Colorado, being the owner.

These few herds mentioned are merely illustrations of the great wealth in the business.

10

THE EXISTING CATTLE COMPANIES
ARE PROSPEROUS, AND NEW ONES
ARE CONSTANTLY BEING FORMED

THE CATTLE BUSINESS, carried on in a small way, as it was in the former days, would pay to-day just as well as ever, only with the difference that it takes a little more capital to start. The cattle are dearer than in former days, and landed proprietorship has become a necessity for the business; still, people have learned that, if more capital is brought into the business, it can be carried on to better advantage. The smaller herds have gradually disappeared, their owners either forming partnerships with one another or selling out to larger companies.

The advantages of large companies, or very large herd-owners over small ones, result from the fact that large operators can make greater savings than small operators.

A man having 1,000 head of cattle will require during the whole year at least two herders, and in the busy seasons, or six months in the year, probably two more, which is equivalent to three for the whole year. A man with 5,000 head only needs two for the whole year, and about six more for six months, equivalent to five for the whole year.

In this item the proportion of expenses between the man owning 1,000 head and the one owning 5,000 head would be three to five. So, where the small owner pays three dollars, the larger owner, who has five times as much capital invested, would pay five dollars, whereas, with the same ratio, he would pay fifteen dollars. When the investment is still larger, the savings is greater.

Buyers can now obtain all the cattle they want from one or two herds, whereas in former days they were compelled to ride all over the country, buying a few head here and a few there, which was an expense and a great loss of time. Consequently, a large buyer can buy cheaper, or at least save expense, in buying his herd.

The large capitalist is independent. He can wait for the highest market prices in Chicago, New York, or New Orleans, and can contract directly with those markets. Large shippers obtain better rates from the railroads than those who ship but a car load or so during the year.

For the last six to ten years Eastern and European

capitalists, who desire more profit from their capital than their own fatherland offers them, have been making constant investments in Western enterprises, such as mining, sheep- and cattle-raising.

Between mining and cattle-raising there lies a contrast, but no comparison.

In mining, the investors may get rich in a few months. But even with the best and safest mines, there remains an element of uncertainty, which may be exciting to the stock-gamblers and to the speculative mind but certainly is very unsatisfactory to the more prudent investor.

Investments in shares of a properly managed livestock company are nothing else than investments in a co-operative farming operation, in which exclusive attention is given to that single branch of farming which is the safest and most profitable.

There is not the slightest element of uncertainty in cattle-raising.

Large and continued operations have proved this fact. Numbers of mining companies have failed to pay; but no livestock company has ever failed to pay large dividends after it had been established long enough to begin selling cattle. On the contrary, it is a known fact that many persons have made princely fortunes from this business.

England, above all other European nations, has done well in entering upon the Western cattle business. It is calculated that England alone has invested $14,000,-000 in the West in cattle and lands; and all their companies, without exception, have been profitable to the shareholders, in some cases paying as much as 30 per cent. As a consequence of this, new companies are constantly being organized. The English have as great confidence in cattle-raising in the West, 6,000 miles away, as have cowboys on the prairies, who have grown up in the business and who daily see its rapid and safe increase.

The president of the Colorado Cattle-Growers' Association, in an address before that body, delivered in January, 1883, said:

During the past year vast sums of foreign capital have been invested in our Western ranges and herds, and it looks to-day as though these large companies would eventually own and control the bulk of the cattle interests of this country. They are fully aware of the great profits of the business, and can control large sums of money, which is bringing but small returns to the owners where it now is, and which, invested in cattle and ranges, will return them double and treble what it is now producing. We cordially invite those new-comers to join with us for the mutual good and protection of our common interests.

The Existing Cattle Companies Are Prosperous

In May, 1883, Scotch cattle companies operating in this Far West were quoted as follows:

Number of shares	Amount of share	Amount paid per share	Name	Price	Average dividend and bonus
	£	£		£	£
42,000	5	5	Hansford Land and Cattle Co., Limited	106/6	New Co.
30,000	10	5	Matador Land and Cattle Co., Limited	115/	New Co.
12,500	10	5	Prairie Cattle Co., Limited	9 7/8	27 5/6
25,000	10	5	Prairie Cattle Co., Limited 2nd issue	9 3/4	27 5/6
12,500	10	5	Prairie Cattle Co., Limited, 3rd issue	9 7/8	*
40,000	5	3 5/8	Powder River Cattle Co., Limited	84/9	New Co.
10,000	10	10	Powder River Cattle Co., preferred 10 per cent	11½	New Co.
24,000	10	5	Texas Land and Cattle Co., Limited	6½	15
16,000	5	5	West. Land and Cattle Co., Limited	7	20
4,500	5	5	West. Land and Cattle Co., Limited, new	7	—
16,000	5	5	West. Land and Cattle Co., Limited preferred	4 5/8	5
4,500	5	5	West. Land and Cattle Co., Limited, preferred new	4 9/16	—
9,000	10	7, 10	Wyoming Cattle Ranche Co.	8× new	6/8 per share

*19½ previous year.

61

11

CHOICE RANGES FOR BREEDING
AND FATTENING CATTLE—
THE ADVANTAGES FROM HAVING
A SUFFICIENT NUMBER OF GOOD BULLS

PEOPLE looking over the map of this vast Western pasture region, a strip 5,600 miles long by 200 wide, will certainly ask whether there is any choice between the various parts as to the selection of a range.

This territory, from north to south, lies between a good many degrees of latitude, and there must be some difference between the summer and winter in the South and the North.

There is a considerable difference in the average temperature, and in each there are extremes of climate which must be detrimental to cattle-raising. But experience shows that too great heat is not good for the fattening of cattle, and a colder summer, and even a colder winter, makes cattle in the Northern states thrive better and fatten quicker than in the Southern.

To illustrate the difference, we will give the statement of Mr. James M. Wilson, one of the most experienced and successful stockmen of Colorado, whose principal business it is to buy steers in the South, drive them north, and to fatten them there until they are ready for the market. He says: "A three-year-old fat steer in the south of Texas weighs 900 to 950 pounds; in the north of Texas, 1,100 pounds; in New Mexico and south and middle Colorado, 1,100 pounds; while in Wyoming, and still farther north in Montana, 1,200 to 1,300 pounds."

Such a difference would decide every one at once in favor of Wyoming or Montana in locating a cattle range. Still, there are more stock ranges south of Wyoming than north of it. I do not wish to say that Wyoming and Montana have not as good ranges as Colorado or New Mexico; on the contrary, Wyoming and Montana are considered as very favorable locations by many, and especially by those who improve their stock, acclimate them, and give them care and attention in the winter, and thereby make this stock much fatter and receive more money for them. But the expense is much greater in herding and watching their animals in the winter. The losses on winter-dropped calves, and on young yearling mothers, constitute in the Northern states the principal percentage of loss; but on the Southern ranges this

63

is nominal. An animal, until it is one year or one and a half years old, thrives and develops faster on the Southern ranges, while on the Northern it advances more slowly and there is always more risk of losing it by storms. Still, the average percentage losses of stock-raising in these Northern states does not exceed 3 per cent, and many stockmen claim that during many winters they have not lost more than 1 per cent.

As a conclusion, I would state that many old and experienced cattlemen are of the opinion that, for the purpose of raising stock—that is, for the increase—the Southern states are the more preferable, while for the business done exclusively, or at least principally, with steers and without much attention to the increase, the Northern states are preferable.

I would prefer the happy medium, such as the country in the southern portion of Colorado and the northern portion of New Mexico. Here the winters are very mild, losses from that cause are insignificant, and the beef will fatten to a good weight. In Montana, which is the latest district in which cattle-raising and fattening has been proved a great success, we find principally Eastern men with capital and good business ability. They, studying the interest of the future cattle business, found the necessity of rearing better stock, and paid much attention to that subject, and therefore we find in Montana perhaps the best-bred herds. They were recruited to a great extent from Eastern States, Iowa, Minnesota, and Wisconsin.

The demand for young cattle for Dakota and Montana ranges is so great now that large numbers are being shipped in by railroads from Minnesota, Iowa, and Wisconsin.

This improvement of stock, a great source of the profit of the cattle-raiser, was in former years not at all understood. The truth is that the ranchmen of old were generally free-and-easy, careless fellows, of no very thorough business training or knowledge.

Their cattle were making money for them surely and with most gratifying rapidity. They cared little or nothing for details, and thought not of improvements, and were not fond enough of any kind of mental labor to study how to increase their very great profits from their herds. They even refused or neglected to breed for better stock, and sold their cows for less than their steers.

It was not until men of money and of good business habits took hold of this business that prices of cattle began to advance. The capitalists gradually bought herd after herd and ranch after ranch, and started in to improve both, and nearly doubled the prices of the old native cattle.

Now, how did they effect this increase of price? In the greatly improved quality of cattle, due to the liberal use of bulls of good blood, is to be found one very great cause of the rise in value of stock cattle.

A few years ago most of the herds were not much better than the original Spanish cattle of Texas and Mexico; but now there is to be observed a great change for the better. The cattle seem to be of superior stock and carry the characteristics of Shorthorns and Herefords. They are perhaps 50 per cent more valuable than their Spanish, Mexican, and Texas progenitors.

What a difference this improving makes, and what a profit therefrom arises to the owner, I will now illustrate.

An old native Texas steer, when matured, weighs, on an average, 800 to 1,000 pounds, worth, say, two and three quarters to three cents per pound in Chicago. A son of a Texas cow crossed with a well-bred bull of Durham, Hereford, or other good breed, will weigh when three years old from 1,100 to 1,300 pounds, and sell for from four to five cents per pound. A four-year-old Texas steer will weigh 1,000 pounds, worth three cents per pound, while a son of a Texas cow by a Shorthorn or Hereford bull three years old will weigh 1,300 pounds, worth from four to five cents per pound.

From this it is easy to perceive the profit which

arises from the use of good stock and blooded bulls. The Hereford breed is by many considered the best for the cross; they are better feeders, hardier, and can stand the winters better than Durhams.

Another necessity is the liberal use of bulls, and on this will depend considerably the profits of the business.

Although the owners of herds are compelled by law to keep one bull for every twenty-five cows, this matter is very difficult of control, and formerly many a small owner did not own a bull at all, and relied simply on his neighbor's bull, with which his cows were grazed. How important it is to have as many good bulls as possible is easy to be seen.

One bull can only serve a certain number of cows, and if there are not bulls enough there is simply no increase; while, on the other hand, if there is one good bull kept with every twenty or twenty-five cows, the increase will be as full as nature allows.

Bulls have in the last five years been shipped from the Eastern states in great numbers, which is only a consequence of the more business-like management of the business.

The ranchman should raise his own bulls if possible. They will be acclimated and do better and more satis-factory service at once, while imported one-year-old bulls cost more at first, are not so reliable for service, and have to get acclimated.

The cost of raising bulls, after the purchase of one good thoroughbred bull and a number of high-graded cows, will not be any more than the cost of raising of any other animal. It only necessitates fencing up the bull and the cows together and away from the others. But the additional cost of fencing will be counter-balanced by the milk these good cows will give.

The use of yearling bulls is, I think, an abuse of nature, and the modern cattle-owner should not count on much benefit arising from bulls of that age; consequently he should exclude them from his calculations when he estimates how many bulls are needed for his herd.

They certainly cannot be confined without incurring expense, but their progeny is weak and likely to die. It is the same with the progeny of the heifers of two years; it would be better if such births could be avoided, as loss of the calves of these two-year heifers, and often of the heifers themselves, is the consequence, especially in the Northern states.

It does undoubtedly pay best to employ the largest, best-formed, and best-bred bulls with one's herd. A bull that has the capacity to reproduce his prominent beef characteristics, such that can give size to his progeny, that is full-bodied, broad-backed, with heavy ham, and has a good constitution, is the bull which will pay the largest profits to the owner

12

PROFITS IN CATTLE-RAISING,
AND FORTUNES MADE THEREIN

THE IMMENSE PROFITS which have been universally realized in the Western cattle business for the past, and which will be increased in the future, owing to the more economical methods pursued, so long as ranges can be purchased at present prices, may seem incredible to many of my readers, who, no doubt, have considered the stories of the fortunes realized as myths. Yet it is true that many men who started only a few years ago with comparatively few cattle, are now wealthy, and, in some cases, millionaires. They certainly did not find the gold upon the prairies, nor did they have any source of revenue beyond the increase of their cattle. The agencies producing this immense wealth are very natural and apparent.

The climate of the West is the healthiest on the

earth; the pure, high mountain air and dry atmosphere are the natural remedies, or rather preventives, against sickness among cattle in general, and against all epidemic diseases in particular; for "nowhere in the Western states do we find any traces of pleuro-pneumonia, foot or mouth, and such like contagious diseases."

The pure, clear water of the mountain rivers affords to cattle another health preserver, and the fine nutritious and bountiful grasses, and in winter the naturally cured hay, furnish to them the healthiest natural food.

Formerly these pastures cost nothing, and at present only a trifle, as I explained in a former chapter, so that the interest on the investment in purchasing land is of little importance in the estimate of the cost of keeping a herd. In fact, ownership of land is now indispensable for a herd-owner. This land in less than ten years will be a considerable factor in the profits of the cattle business, as the value of pastures will constantly increase.

The principal cost of raising cattle is only the herding and watching the cattle by herders, without any cost for sheltering or feeding. In time even these expenses will be reduced, as now already herds are kept in large fenced ranges, and many of the herders are dispensed with.

The losses of cattle, as shown by statistics, are larger among Eastern and European herds, which are sheltered in stables and fed the whole year round, than among the shelterless herds of the West.

The losses in the West to the causes where I shall devote a chapter, are practically reduced by long experience to a certain percentage, which enables the stockmen to calculate infallibly the profits and losses of their business.

This annual loss is found to average 2 to 3 per cent. We may safely put the loss in the extreme Northern states at about 3 per cent, and in the more Southern and temperate districts at 2 or less per cent.

The annual cost of herding the cattle, as I have shown in a previous chapter, is about $.70 per head; adding the other expenses, such as taxes, loss of interest on the purchase-money of land, etc., we find that the entire annual expense is less than $1.50 per head.

It takes a heifer calf, say, three years to mature, and a steer calf will be ready for the market in four years. The latter will then bring $40.00; deducting the $6.00 of expense for his rearing, we have a net profit of $34.00 on each steer.

Now let me illustrate the profits realized from one Texas cow, worth $30.00. In ten years she will have eight calves, which, if they are all steers, will have produced at the end of fourteen years $320, or a profit of

$272.00. The cow herself still remains, and is worth about her original cost for the butcher. These figures are made without reference to any increase in the value of cattle or beef, and without reference to any improvement of the stock by crossing it with better blood.

The next thing to consider is the natural increase of cattle. I will give my opinion first, and then state those of some of the most experienced cattlemen.

I think that 75 or 80 per cent of the cows will drop one calf each year, and that the mortality among these calves will be affected by the mildness or rigor of the climate. The loss of winter-born calves is very small in the Southern portion of the country, but increases as you go north. Therefore I conclude that, for breeding purposes, a more southerly located range is preferable. With the liberal use of bulls, which means at least one bull for every twenty-five cows, which should be strong and well developed, this increase of 75 to 80 per cent may be relied upon. Besides this, the barren and aged cows should be sold at once.

This percentage is to be understood with reference to cows and heifers which are three years of age or more when they drop their first calf.

It is estimated that 40 per cent of heifers when only two years old will produce calves, but I hold this increase to be detrimental to the interest of stock-raising, and I would, when managing a herd, try all means possible to prevent such premature increase.

Few persons realize how rapidly cattle would multiply if all the female progeny were allowed to breed each year. If 100 cows and their female progeny be kept at breeding for ten years, the result would be as follows:

Estimating the natural increase at 80 per cent, of which 40 per cent of the cows would have heifers, which would, beginning when two years old, in their turn have young:

						Heifers
100	cows	in	first	year	drop	40
100	”	”	second	”	”	40
140	”	”	third	”	”	56
180	”	”	fourth	”	”	72
236	”	”	fifth	”	”	94
308	”	”	sixth	”	”	123
402	”	”	seventh	”	”	161
525	”	”	eighth	”	”	210
686	”	”	ninth	”	”	274
896	”	”	tenth	”	”	358
Total, ten years						1,428

The number of steers would be the same as that of heifers, 1,428. Total increase, 2,856.

From this deduct an annual loss of 3 per cent of the number of cattle on hand, and make another deduction for the reason that cows will only average 8 calves in ten years; take your original price of 100 cows, deduct for the keeping of the same $1.50 per head per annum, and you will find an enormous increase and an immense sum representing the value of the cattle on hand, and will learn at what rate the capital in the livestock business increases.

The last factor is the general increase in the value of meat. This I shall explain in my next chapter.

Finally, let me recapitulate all the natural agencies causing the immense profits in this industry by briefly summing them up:

1. Natural increase of cows.

2. Increase of steers for the market.

3. Profit from the yearly advance in weight of the animal until maturity.

4. Profit caused by the improvement of stock by crossing with better breeds.

5. Profit from future increase in the value of beef.

6. Increase in value of the pasture lands owned.

7. Profit from breeding one's own bulls.

13

INSTANCES OF PROFITS REALIZED

JUST AS THE CATTLEMEN of the West are in business upright, honest, and accommodating, so they are in private life courteous and estimable, and to these traits I am indebted for the information concerning instances of success which I will now mention.

Through the courtesy of his foreman, who has been with him for eleven years, I learned the particulars of Mr. F. P. Ernest's unusual success.

Mr. Ernest is the cattle king of Colorado, owning the largest herd in the state.

This gentleman, a Texan-born, came to New Mexico in 1871 with $1,800 and engaged in the business. He had accumulated by 1875 a herd of 6,800 head, which he removed the same year to Colorado. He bought near Deer Trail, on one of the tributaries to the Platte River, enough water front to control a range large enough for his future business, and this location enables him to control 1,500,000 acres of pasture.

His herd has grown, by natural increase and by fortunate purchases, which his foresight and judgment enabled him to make from time to time, to 36,000 head.

Last year he sold about $200,000 worth of beef. He has been offered for his herd, with range and privileges, $850,000, but he declined this offer.

One of the first men to engage in cattle-raising was R. G. Webster, of Denver. He has not only been very successful, but has also become prominent among the cattlemen by his devotion to and furtherance of all the interests of the cattle business in the West.

He began in 1872, in Colorado, with 35 head and $500 in cash. Being unacquainted with the business when he began, he devoted all his time and energy to it, and made himself conversant with all its details and managed it with such skill, both in buying and selling, that he was enabled one year ago to sell his interest for $135,000.

Mr. George A. Binkelman, of Denver, began business in 1868 on the Kiowa, east of Denver, with 100 head of all ages and both sexes. He thinks that from the first his natural increase was 80 per cent annually, none of which he lost, because he was careful to keep his herd together. In the fall of 1875 he removed his herd to the Republican River, farther north; it had increased to 1,200 head.

During the first year after his arrival there, Indians and buffalo-hunters set the prairie on fire, by which most of his herd was scattered and lost. This caused him a great loss of time and business opportunities before he could collect his herd again. Nevertheless, he has now on his range 8,000 head of cattle, mostly steers.

From time to time he bought one piece of water front after the other, and owns now about twenty miles of water front, controlling all the range contiguous to it.

He thinks that the profit of 25 per cent per annum is the minimum the cattle business will yield. During all the time he has also invested, from the profits of this business, in real estate in Denver, and is now the owner of quite a number of houses and lots.

Another prominent and experienced cattleman now living in Denver is Mr. Alfred Butters. He has been engaged principally in buying, fattening, and selling steers. His last transaction was the following:

He bought 2,900 head of two- and three-year-old Texan steers at the cost of $42,000, including horses, saddles, and camp outfit. He held them two years, and sold them for $110,000.

These cattle were shipped and sold at the markets of

Kansas City and Chicago.

Mr. Butters reckons the usual profits of the cattle business, above all expenses and losses, at 25 to 30 per cent per annum, but says that, owing to the advance in the price of cattle, which nearly doubled during the same period indicated, profits were from 50 to 60 per cent.

This advance was measurably due to the improved methods of handling and marketing the product, and the increased demand for beef for consumption, caused by increased exportation, the canning of beef, and the increasing American population.

His range was located both in Indian Territory and Colorado.

He considers that, in order to carry on business, every cattleman must in the future own his own range.

Another very striking example of profits and fortune made in cattle-raising is the experience of Mr. Day, of Wolf Creek, Indian Territory. In 1875 he invested $15,000 in Texas stock, and at the end of six years (two years ago) he sold his herd, not including any land, for $450,000, and offered, after the contract was made, $10,000 bonus to the buyer to release him from his contract.

No outside money was put into the business during these six years.

The following is a statement of the business of a banker of Denver, who does not wish his name thus advertised:

In 1878 he bought 320 head of cattle for	$ 4,000
In 1879 he bought 1,000 head of cattle for	10,000
In 1880 he bought 1,900 head of cattle for	20,000
In 1882 he bought 1,900 head of cattle for	38,500
	$72,500
Horses and ranch	3,500
Total	$76,000
In 1880 he sold steers for	$ 5,500
In 1881 he sold steers for	13,000
In 1882 he sold steers for	27,500
In 1883 he sold steers for	150,000
Total	$196,000

The net profit of his business in five years was $120,000.

Ten years ago an Irish servant-girl wanted money due her, amounting to $150, from a cattle-raiser who lived in Montana. Cattle had been dull, and he could not dispose of any of his herd, but agreed to her to brand fifteen cows in her name, give her the increase, and carry them with his herd, free of cost, until she was ready to sell, he to have the first privilege of purchase. She accepted, held on to her purchase, and last May sold out to her master for $25,000.

80

14

PROFITS TO ACCRUE
FROM A PROPOSED PLAN

IN THE LAST CHAPTER I have spoken of the fortunes made by various individuals, but I was not able to obtain the details of their business from year to year.

Some of my readers may now inquire whether such fortunes can still be made.

Prior to answering this question, I would state that the fortunes made in this business have not always been due solely to the natural increase of stock, but often greatly to good judgment and management, which led to the purchase of ranches while the land was very cheap, and which utilized the state of the market in making purchases and sales, and which suggested the liberal borrowing of money to increase the investment.

Since it was very well known that the cattle business is very safe, and that the larger the capital therein the greater the ratio of profit, as the expenses do not increase at the same rate with the capital, the cattle-raiser has found no difficulty in borrowing an amount of money equal to his investment; and, though he might pay from 10 to 15 per cent per annum for the use of it, yet he might fairly expect to realize therefrom 25 to 35 per cent.[1]

I have repeatedly figured the profits to be made in the business, according to various investments, and I will now give to my readers the details of a plan with an investment of $250,000, which should double itself in five years, and then begin to increase in a still more striking way.

I will first state all the conditions which I deem necessary for the economical management of the business:

In the first place, I would select and purchase a favorably situated home range, large enough to keep most of the first herd, with its prospective increase, for some years, and also so situated as to control a large area of public land for the use of my cattle.

By a favorable spot I understand a climate where breeding can be most profitably carried on. Such a range should lie south of the thirty-eighth degree of latitude (about Pueblo), where the winters are mild, and no dan-

[1] How safe the cattle business is considered will be seen from the fact that banks will loan more money to a cattleman, in proportion to his investment, and at less interest, than to the richest merchants.

ger exists of losing any percentage of calves or young animals from exposure.

The quantity and quality of the grass, and the natural shelter for the cattle against storms, should also be considered in such selection.

I would fence such a tract at once, which would cost about seventy-five dollars per mile and allow us to dispense with some of the herders. I would also fence off therefrom smaller pastures for sick and for highbred cattle and for breeding bulls. In view of the certain future increase in the value of lands, I would invest even as much as $100,000 in the same, for though they will not yield any yearly profits, yet they will in the end be very profitable.

In view of the ascertained fact that beef will fatten more rapidly and thrive better on the Northern prairies, where they are not bothered by the heat, and have a chance to acquire fat rapidly, I would keep a lookout for another range farther north, to be bought from the profits of the business, after the steers have become more numerous from natural increase.

We must then select the herd, and, in this connection, we must decide upon the breed and upon the proportion between the steers and the cows.

I would select Texas stock and, for breeding purposes, good grade Durham or Hereford bulls.

If the capital invested is expected to pay a dividend from the first year, I would buy steers which, with a year's growth, would help to pay such dividend. Otherwise I would prefer to grow my own cattle for market. The latter course I consider to be preferable—that is, to wait two or three years before marketing any cattle.

I would raise my own bulls from full-blooded stock, and would keep one for every twenty-five or thirty cows. Such bulls would cost about ten dollars each, whereas those bought from the East cost about fifty dollars to one hundred dollars each, and, not being acclimated, are not so reliable.

Of course, originally, I must buy enough bulls for the herd—that is, one for every twenty-five cows.

Cows proved to be barren or too aged to be profitable for breeding I would sell at once.

I will now make a statement of the estimated business for six years, premising that, under favorable conditions supposed, 80 per cent of the cows will have calves each year, and that the annual loss from all causes will not exceed 2 per cent of the cattle, and may even be reduced to a smaller ratio. I would also state that the calves are about equally divided in sex, as experience shows.

In this statement I consider that, at three years of age, heifers become cows.

Profits to Accrue from a Proposed Plan

INVESTMENT IN REAL ESTATE

30,000 acres, at $2.50	$75,000
Fencing, building, equipment	5,000
Total	$80,000

INVESTMENT IN STOCK

1,000 cows with 500 [2] calves, at $30	$30,000
1,000 two-year-old heifers, at $25	25,000
1,000 yearling heifers, at $20	20,000
1,000 three-year-old steers, at $33	33,000
1,000 two-year-old steers, at $25	25,000
1,000 one-year-old steers, at $20	20,000
100 graded bulls, at $50	5,000
1 full-blooded bull	250
40 good-graded cows, at $50	2,000
50 horses, at $50	2,500
1 mule team, wagon, and harness	500
Saddles and equipment for horses	250
	$163,500
Balance, cash on hand	7,500
Capital stock paid up	$250,000

[2] The proportion of calves is reduced, because these cows must be driven to their new pasture grounds, and many of the calves born during the drive may be expected to die.

Statement at the End of the First Year, January 1

STOCK ACCOUNT

Value of livestock:
2,000 cows (less 2 per cent loss=1,960),
   at $30 $58,800

1,000 two-year-old heifers (less 2 per cent loss=980), at $25	24,500
250 yearling heifers (less 2 per cent loss=245), at $20	4,900
800 heifer calves, at $12	9,600
1,000 three-year-old steers (less 2 per cent loss=980), at $33	32,340
1,000 two-year-old steers (less 2 per cent loss=980), at $25	24,500
250 yearling steers (less 2 per cent loss=245), at $20	4,900
300 purchased during the year, at $17	5,100
800 steer calves, at $12	9,600
100 graded bulls (less 2 per cent loss=98), at $50	4,900
1 blooded bull	250
40 graded cows (less 2 per cent loss=39), at $50	1,950
50 horses, at $50	2,500
1 mule team, etc	500
Saddles and equipment for horses	250
18 high-graded calves, at 25	450
	$185,040
Value of real estate	80,000
Total	265,000
Capital stock	250,000
	$15,040

CASH ACCOUNT

Balance brought forward	$7,500

Cash from sale of 1,000 four-year-old steers
(less 2 per cent loss=980), at $40   39,200

Total	$46,700

EXPENSE ACCOUNT

Salaries for manager, foreman, herders, their supplies and incidentals	$7,000
Taxes on cattle	1,000
300 yearling steers bought at $17	5,100
Paid 7 per cent dividend on $250,000	17,500
	$30,600
Cash on hand	$16,100
Increased value of stock	15,040
Cash on hand	16,100
Undivided surplus	$31,140

At the end of the first year's business we see that we can pay a larger dividend than 7 per cent; but we need more yearling steers, and possibly more two-year-olds, to keep up our stock.

In order to meet the item of salaries, I will henceforth charge, in the expense account, one dollar against each head of stock therefor, though it is possible it will in reality be a little less.

Statement at the End of the Second Year, January 1
STOCK ACCOUNT

Value of livestock:
2,940 cows (less 2 per cent loss=2,883),
at $30 $86,490

245 two-year-old heifers (less 2 per cent loss=240), at $25	6,000
800 yearling heifers (less 2 per cent loss=784), at $20	15,680
1,153 heifer calves, at $12	13,836
980 three-year-old steers (less 2 per cent loss=960), at $33	32,780
545 two-year-old steers (less 2 per cent loss=534), at $25	13,350
500 two-year-old steers bought during year, at $25	12,500
800 yearling steers (less 2 per cent loss=784), at $20	15,680
1,153 steer calves, at $12	13,836
98 bulls (less 2 per cent loss=96), at $50	4,800
39 graded cows (less 2 per cent loss=38), at $50	1,900
9 graded yearling bulls (less 2 per cent loss=8), at $35	280
9 graded yearling heifers (less 2 per cent loss=8), at $35	280
34 graded calves, at $25	850
50 horses (less 2 per cent loss=49), at $50	2,450
1 mule team, etc., saddles, etc.	750
	$221,462
Value of real estate	80,000
Total	$301,462
Capital stock	250,000
	$51,462

88

CASH ACCOUNT

Balance from last year brought forward	$16,100
Cash from sale, 980 (less 2 per cent loss=960), at $40	38,400
Total	$54,500

EXPENSE ACCOUNT

Salaries, at $1 per head of stock	$9,000
Taxes on land and cattle	2,000
500 two-year-old steers bought during the year, at $25	12,500
Paid 7 per cent dividend on $250,000	17,500
	$41,000
Cash on hand	$13,000
Increased value of stock	$51,462
Cash on hand	13,500
Undivided surplus	$64,962

After the second year 10 per cent dividend may be paid, and we can begin to sell off some of the barren and old cows of the original purchase.

Statement at the End of the Third Year, January 1

STOCK ACCOUNT

Value of livestock:	
2,800 cows, at $30	$84,000
784 two-year-old heifers (less 2 per cent loss= 768), at $25	19,200
1,153 yearling heifers (less 2 per cent loss= 1,130), at $20	22,600
1,120 heifer calves, at $12	13,440

89

1,034 three-year-old steers, (less 2 per cent loss=1,014), at $33	33,462
784 two-year-old steers (less 2 per cent loss=768), at $25	19,200
1,153 yearling steers (less 2 per cent loss=1,130), at $20	22,600
1,120 steer calves, at $12	13,440
96 bulls, original (less 2 per cent loss=94), at $50	4,700
38 high-graded cows (less 2 per cent loss=37), a $50	1,850
8 own-raised bulls, at $50	400
8 own-raised two-year-old heifers, at $40	320
17 own-raised yearling bulls (less 2 per cent loss=16), at $35	560
17 own-raised graded yearling heifers (less 2 per cent loss=16), at $35	560
34 graded calves, at $25	850
49 horses (less 2 per cent loss=48), at $50	2,400
1 mule team, saddles, etc.	750
400 two-year-old steers bought during the year at $25	10,000
20 horses bought during the year, at $50	1,000
	$251,332
Value of real estate	80,000
Total	$331,332
Capital stock	250,000
	$81,332

Profits to Accrue from a Proposed Plan

CASH ACCOUNT

Balance from last year brought forward	$13,500
Cash from sale of 960 steers (less 2 per cent loss=940), at $40	37,600
Cash from sale of 258 barren and old cows as beef, at $30	7,740
Total	$58,840

EXPENSE ACCOUNT

Salaries, at $1 per head	$9,000
Taxes on land and cattle	2,000
400 two-year-old steers bought, at $25	10,000
20 horses bought, at $50	1,000
Paid dividend, 10 per cent on $250,000	25,000
	$47,000
Cash on hand	$11,840
Increased value of stock	$81,332
Cash on hand	$11,840
Undivided surplus	$93,172

Statement at the End of the Fourth Year, January 1

STOCK ACCOUNT

Value of livestock:

3,568 cows (less 2 per cent loss=3,500), at $30	$105,000
1,130 two-year-old heifers (less 2 per cent loss=1,108), at $25	27,700
1,120 yearling heifers (less 2 per cent loss=1,100), at $20	22,000
1,400 heifer calves, at $12	16,800

1,168 three-year-old steers (less 2 per cent loss=1,144), at $33	37,752
1,130 two-year-old steers (less 2 per cent loss=1,108), at $25	27,700
1,120 yearling steers (less 2 per cent loss=1,100), at $20	22,000
1,400 steer calves, at $12	16,800
94 bulls (less 2 per cent loss=92), at $50	4,600
45 high-graded cows (less 2 per cent loss=44), at $50	2,200
24 own-raised bulls (less 2 per cent loss=23), at $50	1,150
17 own-raised yearling bulls (less 2 per cent loss=16), at $35	560
40 graded calves, at $25	1,000
68 horses (less 2 per cent loss=66), at $50	3,300
1 mule team, saddles, etc.	750
400 two-year-old steers bought during the year at $25	10,000
	$300,472
Value of real estate	80,000
Total	$380,472
Capital stock	250,000
	$130,472

CASH ACCOUNT

Balance from last year brought forward	11,840
Cash from sale of 1,014 steers (less 2 per cent loss=994), at $40	39,760
Total	$51,600

Profits to Accrue from a Proposed Plan

EXPENSE ACCOUNT

Salaries, at $1 per head	$9,000
Taxes on land and cattle	2,000
400 two-year-old steers bought, at $25	10,000
Paid dividend of ten per cent on $250,000	25,000
	$46,000
Cash on hand	$5,600
Increased value of stock	130,472
Cash on hand	5,600
Undivided surplus	$136,072

Statement at the End of the Fifth Year, January 1

STOCK ACCOUNT

Value of livestock:

4,000 cows, at $30	$120,000
1,100 two-year-old heifers (less 2 per cent loss=1,078), at $25	26,950
1,400 yearling heifers (less 2 per cent loss=1,078), at $25	26,950
1,600 heifer calves, at $12	19,200
1,108 three-year-old steers (less 2 per cent loss=1,086), at $33	35,838
1,100 two-year-old steers (less 2 per cent loss=1,078), at $25	26,950
1,400 yearling steers (less 2 per cent loss=1,372), at $20	27,440
1,600 steer calves, at $12	19,200
92 original bulls (less 2 per cent loss=90), at $50	4,500

59 high-graded cows (less 2 per cent loss=58), at $50	2,900
39 own-raised bulls, at $50	1,950
16 own-raised two-year-old heifers, at $40	640
20 own-raised yearling heifers, at $35	700
20 own-raised yearling bulls, at $35	700
55 own-raised high-graded calves, at $25	1,375
66 horses, at $50	3,300
1 mule team, saddle, etc.	750
200 yearling steers bought during the year, at $20	4,000
	$323,833
Value of real estate	80,000
Total	$403,833
Capital stock	250,000
	$153,833

CASH ACCOUNT

Balance from last year brought forward	$5,600
Cash from sale of 1,144 steers (less 2 per cent loss=1,122), at $40	44,880
Cash from sale of 516 cows, at $30	15,480
Total	$65,960

EXPENSE ACCOUNT

Salaries, at $1 per head	$10,000
Taxes on land and cattle	2,000
200 yearling steers bought during year, at $20	4,000
Paid dividend, ten per cent on $250,000	25,000
	$41,000
Cash on hand	24,960

Profits to Accrue from a Proposed Plan

Increased value of stock	$153,833
Cash on hand	24,960
Undivided surplus	$178,793

Statement at the End of the Sixth Year, January 1

STOCK ACCOUNT

Value of livestock:

5,078 cows (less 2 per cent loss=4,970), at $30	$149,100
1,372 two-year-old heifers (less 2 per cent loss=1,344), at $25	33,600
1,600 yearling heifers (less 2 per cent loss=1,568), at $20	31,360
1,988 heifer calves, at $12	23,856
1,078 three-year-old steers (less 2 per cent loss=1,056), at $33	34,848
1,572 two-year-old steers (less 2 per cent loss=1,544), at $25	39,300
1,600 yearling steers, at $12	23,856
149 bulls (less 2 per cent loss=146), at $50	7,300
74 high-graded cows (less 2 per cent loss=72), at $50	3,600
20 high-graded two-year-old heifers, at $40	800
27 yearling bulls, at $35	845
27 yearling heifers at $35	845
60 own-raised high-graded cows, at $25	1,500
66 horses, at $50	3,300
1 mule team, saddles, etc.	750

900 two-year-old steers bought during the year at $25	22,500
	$377,360
Value of real estate	80,000
Total	$457,360
Capital stock	250,000
	$207,360

CASH ACCOUNT

Balance from last year brought forward	$24,960
Cash from sale of 1,086 steers (less 2 per cent loss=1,065), at $40	42,600
Total	$67,560

EXPENSE ACCOUNT

Salaries, at $1 per head	$10,000
Taxes on cattle and land	2,000
900 steers bought, at $25	22,500
Paid dividend of 10 per cent on $250,000	25,000
	$59,500
Cash on hand	$8,060

Increased value of stock	$207,360
Cash on hand	8,060
Undivided surplus	$215,420

At the end of the sixth year I will make a summary statement, and can safely take it for granted that the real estate, with its improvements in six years' time, will have increased at least 50 per cent in value over the price—$80,000 will be worth $120,000.

Profits to Accrue from a Proposed Plan

Summary and Financial Statement Showing Status of Investment at the End of Six Years

STOCK ACCOUNT

Value of livestock on hand		$377,360
Cash on hand, as per cash-book		8,060
Real estate, 50 per cent advance		120,000
Total value of all property		$505,420
Deduct capital stock		250,000
Surplus		$255,420
Add to this—		
Dividends, first year, 7 per cent	$17,500	
Dividends, second year, 7 per cent	17,500	
Dividends, third year, 10 per cent	25,000	
Dividends, fourth year, 10 per cent	25,000	
Dividends, fifth year, 10 per cent	25,000	
Dividends, sixth year, 10 per cent	25,000	
		$135,000

Surplus and cash dividends in six years, being 156 per cent profit on invested capital, $390,420.

Let us now look at the livestock on hand. Every year hereafter there will be sold over 2,000 head of animals, and, as the steers are now of improved breed, they will bring more on the market than forty dollars per head.

As we now have a sufficiency of steers, I consider it expedient to buy a range, either in Colorado or Wyoming, where all steers of one year and a half or more in age can be driven and fattened.

We have sold, during the last six years, 774 old and barren cows; we will sell next year 1,000; and probably the balance of the original stock the next year, in order to keep only an improved herd of cows.

All the improved stock has increased in value, to which increase I have made no reference in the above calculations.

I have shown this statement to a number of old and experienced cattlemen, and they all think that my estimate of profits is reasonable, and, if anything, too low.

From the foregoing statements, I believe, every one will be convinced that no other business is so safe nor so profitable as cattle-raising in the Far West.

15

THE FUTURE OF THE
CATTLE BUSINESS IN THE WEST

NEVER in the history of the cattle business of the West has the future of this industry looked brighter and more promising than at the present time.

Great cattle corporations—with means sufficient for all the wants of the business, and operated by men of great ability, who have studied this industry, and can manage the same in a business-like manner—are rapidly filling up all untaken lands fit for good ranges, and will soon change this Western cattle-raising into a monopoly, as are railroads now in the East. The business of cattle-raising has, in the later years, assumed a different phase, and is managed on better business principles than was the case a few years ago. The wealthy capitalist, when studying the question of national economics, found that the supply of meat for the future had become a serious question. He perceived that the population in America, and that of Europe in a greater degree, was increasing much faster than the cattle; and therefore concluded that more attention to cattle or meat production would have to be given, or the price of meat would go into fabulous figures. He saw, from reports and his own observations, that here were lands and climate, which up to this time were little understood and estimated, where cattle would thrive, and could be raised summer and winter with very little expense. He ascertained that, with small investment and no risk, large fortunes could be made in the business, as was proved by the experience of those pioneers who had already their money therein. Knowing that he would have many followers, he saw the necessity of owning his pasture lands, and of using the best skill in their management and improvement, so that he could obtain now full profits of his investments. The study of the cattle interests suggested several changes. In order to compete with the other markets of the world, it was found expedient to improve the stock by crossing them with better breeds, and thereby make their meat better both in taste and quality, and enable the owners to realize higher prices by the sale thereof.

Formerly, all a stock-owner required was the location of a range, with water and grass sufficient for his herd. It mattered not whether he was the owner of it or not, just as long as he was the first to occupy it as a range. Under the loose conditions his herd grew from hundreds to thousands, and he found himself in a few years a wealthy man. He sold his cattle and ranches for far less than they were really worth. He did not care much for the improvement of his stock, and now, when he buys in again, he finds that all has changed.

Lands are now increased in value, and it has become evident that a man must own the lands upon which his ranch is located. More care and business economies have to be practiced to meet these new conditions. The bringing of more capital into the business, the principles of economy now practiced, and the improvements now made, have entirely changed the cattle-raising business, making it a more legitimate one, and of good standing and importance. And surely I do not know of any other legitimate, safe business that will yield as certain and large returns as the cattle business in the West, where the laws of the different states seem to be made entirely for the benefit of the stockman, and where all the requirements necessary are the practice of economy and the improvement of the native stock.

But, referring now to its future, and bearing in mind that, in view of the increasing population of America and Europe, we need fear no overproduction, we may conclude that there will always be a ready market, at good figures.

A favorable year yields the farmer large crops, but he can not get high prices for the same, while, with a poor harvest, he gets better prices, but has not enough to sell. Not so in the cattle business; although the markets may fluctuate a trifle, still every one knows that these fluctuations have, for the last forty years, always gone upward; and, since the necessity of a larger increase in the number of cattle, in order to supply the present and rapidly increasing populations of the world, is fully recognized everywhere, we may safely conclude that the price of meat will be constantly on an increase for years to come.

In a former chapter I quoted a report by J. Berger, Spencer & Co., of London and Manchester, England, stating the price of meat there for American beef, and the still-increasing demand for the same.

This increasing demand in Europe for American cattle requires attention of the breeders to improvement of their cattle, in order to compete with the Danish, Dutch, and Russian beef in taste, so that the same price may be obtained.

This improving of herds has been practiced during recent years, and I have already shown in the last chapter how much more profit for the owner lies in this improvement.

In the same reports of J. Berger, Spencer & Co., the shipment and export of dressed meat were mentioned. This is an invention of late years, and adds another new factor to the profits of the business of the future. The refrigerator system is not yet commonly introduced, but I risk the opinion that, in less than ten years, no live cattle except for breeding purposes, will be shipped across the Atlantic, or across long distances of land by rail.

In Texas and the Far West all export cattle will be killed and dressed at home, and then shipped in refrigerator cars.

And what profit for the cattle-owner lies in that?

The shipping of stock is wasteful and expensive. The cattle are bruised, and lose invariably flesh and fat, while some of them are trampled to death in the cars. The freight on live cattle is 50 per cent higher than on dressed beef, and the breeder will realize right at home the highest market return for his animals.

The refrigerator meat is not only as good, but it is even superior to the freshly slaughtered meat of shipped live cattle. When it lies on the block in the market it is rosy and red, like wax, while meat of freshly slaughtered cattle is shriveled up and flabby in comparison with

it. These slaughter houses with refrigerator establish-
ments combined are of late much talked about; the refrigerator machines seem as perfect as possible, and it
will be but a few years till, in the different parts of the
Far West, there will be many in operation, instead of
only a few just at present. There is no reason why the
West should not supply all the dressed meat direct. And
what will be the profit therefrom?

In summing up the future of the cattle business, we
conclude that no business in the world has brighter pros-
pects, both as to safety in investment and in the amount
of profit it will secure.

The consular agent of this country at Crefeld, Germany, Mr. Potter, in a recent communication to the
State Department at Washington, discusses the question of the increase of population in Europe, the possibility of increasing agricultural products, and the growing
dependence upon foreign countries for food. He says
that, in spite of the relief afforded by the emigration of so
large numbers, there is a constantly increasing tendency
to over population, while the food-producing capacity
has about reached its limit in most of the European
countries. The grain crop of Europe for 1883 is estimated to fall short of the demands for home consumption by more than 350,000,000 bushels. The deficiency in
meat supply is about measured by that of the bread sup-

ply. This represents conditions on the present basis of population. But the annual increase in population is about 1½ per cent, or 16 per cent in ten years. This amounts to 3,325,000 annually, or 36,000,000 in the ten years to be fed, above the present population, without, as he thinks, any material increase in the production of food. He calculates it will require annually 335,-199,116 bushels of wheat and 13,138,832 head of cattle, averaging 1,000 pounds live weight, or their equivalent in other food. To measure the deficiency in food in Europe likely to exist in 1892, there must be added the present annual deficiency of over 300,000,000 bushels of breadstuffs, making the total deficiency in breadstuffs over 600,000,000 bushels, with a proportionate amount of meat, which deficiency would be annually enlarged by the natural growth of population, without a corresponding increase of food production.

On the basis of Mr. Potter's conclusions—and that they are correct in the main no one will question—American farmers and stock-raisers need have no fear in regard to a market for their surplus crops or stock above that needed to supply the home demand. Europe will always need all we have to spare, and will pay remunerative prices. It is probable that the increased demand in Europe will fully keep pace with the increased supply from this source. In the production of meats, beef, pork,

105

and mutton, with our broad cornfields and still broader grazing lands, reaching from the Missouri to the Pacific, and the British line on the north to Mexico on the south, where stock range through the year at no expense beyond herding, the American farmer and stock-grower has no competition to fear. He can make meat, and deliver it in the markets of Europe, in competition with any other country on the face of the globe. Along with the increased demand from Europe, growing out of its increase of population, we have an increased home demand due to the same cause. But our increase, instead of being only $1\frac{1}{2}$ per cent per annum, is over 3 per cent, and will bring our population up to over 80,000,000 in 1890, against about 50,000,000 in 1880.

Owing to the general interest of the business, and the increasing population rushing to this Far West country, the public lands are being rapidly appropriated, and their value advancing in the market. Delay, therefore, will be a detriment to the investor.

16

PROGRESS OF THE NEW WEST

ALL THAT TERRITORY between the Missouri River and the Pacific Slope, comprising Wyoming, Colorado, New Mexico, Arizona, Utah, Idaho, and Montana, a portion of Dakota, Nebraska, and Kansas, composes the New West, being nearly one-third of the whole United States. It is about 1,100 miles in length, from north to south, and 1,000 miles in width.

The formation of this region is gradually from east to west, and averages 3,000 to 6,000 feet high. Mountains in parallel chains rise majestically to an elevation of from 8,000 to 15,000 feet, and among them are found parks or plateaux with elevations of from 8,000 to 9,000 feet. The mountains are cut by gullies and cañons, down which the streams, formed by the melting snows, have worn their beds. These streams are the headwaters of the mighty rivers of the Mississippi Valley. At the foot of the mountains are the grass-covered foothills, which add a great charm to the scenery.

The parks in the mountains and the boundless plains constitute the great pastoral region of which I have treated so extensively.

The extensive valleys along the creeks and rivers are susceptible of the highest state of cultivation.

The mountains themselves are rich in deposits of gold, silver, iron, and copper metals.

Among the foothills and in the parks have been found vast deposits of coal.

There is no timber on the plains except that growing along the streams, which is generally cottonwood, box elder, or willows; on the foothills and mountains grow pine, spruce, and cedar in vast quantities, which are excellent for building purposes.

No better climate can be found than that of the New West.

The first immigration into the New West can only be dated as far back as 1858, when parties on their way to California halted at the foot of the Rocky Mountains and began to wash the streams for gold.

It was an unknown country, generally yet believed to be a desert, only inhabited by the red man and wild animals.

Its further development was for some years checked by the Civil War in America, and by the nomadic and warlike Indians who traversed the plains.

In 1867 the railroads pushed their course westward, and with them came immigration, and the hostile tribes of Indians were exterminated or driven to the remote mountain fastnesses. It was then found that the New West abounded in resources of many kinds, and population began to pour in. From 1870 to 1883 it grew to about 1,000,000 souls. Colorado had in 1860, 34,000 people; in 1870, 99,864; in 1880, 195,234. It now numbers over 310,000 people.

The resources of this great West have been understood, in fact, during the last ten years only, and it is safe to conclude that in a few years its population will be counted by millions.

Colorado, in 1870, had 157 miles of railroad. In 1880 there were 1,571 miles, and 1883, 3,100 miles; and new ones being constantly constructed.

Only within the last few years has New Mexico, with its 120,000 square miles, received any attention as a field for immigration and settlement; its manifold resources have not been developed, owing to the want of railroads, but this lack is being supplied rapidly, for railroads are in course of construction in all directions, and immigrants from Eastern states and Europe are arriving in yearly increasing numbers.

In 1879 it had 183 miles of railroad. By 1881, 1,096 miles had been built, and there are now 2,000 miles. The natural characteristics of New Mexico are very similar to those of Colorado.

Prior to the building of railroads all this vast country was inhabited by the Indians, who have now yielded to civilization, and none are to be found in Colorado. All of the tribes are under the immediate charge of the United States Army, and the lawless ones have been removed hundreds of miles to the west and away from civilization.

The original and principal industry of the Far West is mining for gold and silver. The mountains are full of mineral wealth, and many substantial towns and mining camps have grown up among the mountains.

As an illustration of the progress of this industry, I would refer to the statistics of the yearly output of Colorado:

1870, gold, silver, copper, and lead	$2,680,000
1875, gold, silver, copper, and lead	5,434,387
1877, gold, silver, copper, and lead	7,216,283
1878, gold, silver, copper, and lead	10,558,116
1879, gold, silver, copper, and lead	19,110,862
1880, gold, silver, copper, and lead	23,500,000
1881, gold, silver, copper, and lead	22,203,508
1882, gold, silver, copper, and lead	26,750,898

Gilpin County, the smallest county of the state, has produced $36,000,000 in gold, and is to-day as productive as ever. Many of true its fissure veins have been worked to a depth of 1,000 feet or more, and improved in richness with depth.

The iron mines of southern Colorado and northern New Mexico are inexhaustible, and superior coal is found in various sections of Colorado, New Mexico, and Arizona, and other parts of the West.

By reason of these natural resources of the mountains all kinds of smelters, ore-reduction works, and rolling mills have been established, and have vastly increased the wealth of the Western country.

The agricultural industry of the West was at first neglected, and it was thought that but little of the country was fit for cultivation; but it is now found that Colorado and New Mexico alone can feed 10,000,000 people. New Mexico alone has 8,000,000 acres of good agricultural land, well supplied with water. Recent immigration has brought the population of New Mexico up to about 150,000 people. A few years ago three-quarters of the population of New Mexico was Mexican, and spoke the Spanish language. This element will soon be lost in the flood of American population which is now overwhelming them.

Owing to the dryness of the atmosphere all over this

Western country, the natural rainfall is not sufficient for the growth of grain or vegetables, and irrigation must be resorted to. By the construction of large canals, with reservoirs and laterals, the water is easily conducted from the mountain streams over the land, richly repaying the farmer for his time, labor, and expense.

The main canal is taken out high enough up the stream to secure a grade sufficient to carry the water out along the highlands. From this main channel laterals are taken out at convenient distances, while from these furrows are run by the plow to convey the water upon the land. One can easily irrigate eighty acres of small grain, or forty acres of corn or potatoes.

With this process there is no possibility of failure of crops. The farmer applies moisture just when it is needed, and in such quantity as will insure a harvest.

The rains which fall in the spring are often sufficient to germinate the seed and cause it to shoot above the ground, but when the summer comes on, an application of water is necessary.

In the mountain district, where there is much greater rainfall, irrigation is not necessary.

The most productive and most populous portions of the earth are those which have, from time immemorial, relied upon artificial irrigation to grow the food to sustain their people. Egypt, India, Italy, France, Spain, and parts of Asia and Africa, have had recourse to this method, and some of them know no other.

Irrigation in this Western country gives a security to the farmer, and a control over the results of his labor, that nowhere else can be found in any state, east, north, or south; and the very long haul of freight from the nearest agricultural portions of Kansas and Nebraska fully protects the farmer against competition. The great mining interests demand all the produce that the farmers can raise; and the area of farming lands being limited to the capacity of the mountain streams, the prices for the products of the farm will always be high.

Those best adapted for this Western country are wheat, oats, barley, rye, potatoes, and all kinds of vegetables. All small cereals grow here to greater proportion than in any of the Eastern states.

The average yield of wheat is about twenty-five bushels to the acre, but sometimes rises to sixty bushels per acre. I have myself produced as much as sixty bushels of oats and forty-two of barley to the acre.

The native grasses of this Western country make better hay than any other. Alfalfa, a species of lucerne or clover, grows remarkably well; it produces three crops per year, and has been cultivated very extensively during the last six years.

At a time, ten years ago, Colorado had but ten acres

113

sown in wheat, while last year 50,000 acres were reported to be in cultivation; and it is expected that, in five years more, this will be increased to 100,000 acres.

The value of cereals raised, in 1882, in Colorado was $2,500,000.

Farming lands are sold at from five to thirty dollars an acre, depending upon location, convenience to railroads, and nearness to large towns.

Good garden-vegetables ground near Denver sells at from $200 to $500 per acre.

Wyoming and Montana have but few farms, and are best adapted to stock-raising.

Large portions of all these Western territories and states are unfit for cultivation, but all the river valleys, as well as the table lands lying within reach of irrigation, are very productive, the soil being fertile everywhere; and only the scarcity of water prevents the whole West from becoming a garden spot, an agricultural Eden.

All the lands unfit for agriculture make excellent pastures for stock. The rainfall is sufficient for the growth of the grasses, and the dryness of the atmosphere cures them on the stem and affords good winter pastures for the herds.

So soon as all the pasture land is taken up, I believe cattle-raising will become a monopoly, and will be in the hands of a few wealthy capitalists and companies.

In 1870 the cattle on the plains of Colorado numbered only 300,000; to-day they number over 2,000,000, and it is expected that 200,000 more will be driven into the state this year.

Most of the Colorado cattle-growers are wealthy men, and some of them have become millionaires.

Horse-raising has been carried to some extent, but the industry is not yet much developed.

Sheep-raising is the oldest industry in New Mexico, and from there was introduced into Colorado. The original sheep were Mexican, but have been improved by crossing with American. Sheep-raising has proved to be as profitable as cattle-raising, and less capital is required in the business.

The price of sheep is from $1.50 to $3.00 per head. A sheep will shear about two pounds of wool. The American, or graded, wool is worth from three to seven cents per pound more than the common Mexican. Herds of from 1,000 to 2,500 are in charge of one herder.

As in the cattle business, so in the sheep business we find owners of immense herds.

The wool-clip of Colorado in 1870 yielded the sheep-growers but $100,000, while this year's yield will bring them $1,500,000.

With this increasing population of the West, numerous towns and cities have sprung into existence. The pride of the West is Denver, called the "Parlor City," on account of its cleanliness and beauty, or the "Queen City of the Plains." It excites the admiration of all visitors.

For persons of leisure or wealth in this region Denver has many attractions. Many such people have built elegant residences, and the citizens have taken pride in constructing fine public edifices and business blocks; and the city is supplied with all modern improvements, such as the telephone, the electric light, waterworks, and gas. The water supply is supplemented from numerous artesian wells.

Ten years ago Denver had only 10,000 inhabitants; to-day the population is over 75,000. It is growing faster now than at any previous time. It is considered one of the prettiest and best-built cities of the American continent, and yet it is only twenty-four years old. It is the center of science, art, intelligence, and refinement of the West, besides being the most important city, by reason of its commerce. Thirteen different railroad companies center therein, radiating in all directions, and forcing their way through the mountains and opening up all parts of the Western country.

Leadville has 25,000 inhabitants. Founded in 1878, it is a marvel for growth and wealth, being the greatest mining camp in the world.

116

Pueblo is for the West what Pittsburgh is for the East, the center of manufacturing.

Cheyenne is the home of the cattle kings of the northern portion of the West. At a meeting of stock-growers held there in November, 1883, $100,000,000 of property were represented.

Even in New Mexico there are towns of from 10,000 to 12,000 inhabitants, as Las Vegas and Albuquerque, though the immigration has but just begun.

Wherever great inducements are offered you will find adventurous, enterprising, and educated men. In this Western country the number of such people is very great.

It is an admitted fact, too, that Western people are hospitable, open-hearted, and liberal. So one may find on these Western plains the noblest exemplars of manhood.

In what other part of the world, then, are to be found advantages equal to those offered on the central plateau of North America?

of which *Cattle-Raising on the Plains of North America*
is Number 24, was started in 1953 by the University of
Oklahoma Press. It is designed to introduce today's
readers to the exciting events of our frontier past and to
some of the memorable writings about them. The following list is complete as of the date of publication of this
volume:

1. Prof. Thomas J. Dimsdale. *The Vigilantes of Montana*. With an introduction by E. DeGolyer.
2. A. S. Mercer. *The Banditti of the Plains*. With a
   foreword by William H. Kittrell.
3. Pat F. Garrett. *The Authentic Life of Billy, the Kid*.
   With an introduction by Jeff C. Dykes.
4. Yellow Bird (John Rollin Ridge). *The Life and
   Adventures of Joaquín Murieta*. With an introduction by Joseph Henry Jackson.
5. Lewis H. Garrard. *Wah-to-yah and the Taos Trail*.
   With an introduction by A. B. Guthrie, Jr.
6. Charles L. Martin. *A Sketch of Sam Bass, the Ban-
   dit*. With an introduction by Ramon F. Adams.
7. Washington Irving. *A Tour on the Prairies*. With an
   introduction by John Francis McDermott.
8. *X. Beidler: Vigilante*. Edited by Helen Fitzgerald
   Sanders in collaboration with William H. Bertsche,
   Jr. With a foreword by A. B. Guthrie, Jr.

9. Nelson Lee. *Three Years Among the Comanches.* With an introduction by Walter Prescott Webb.

10. *The Great Diamond Hoax and Other Stirring Incidents in the Life of Asbury Harpending.* With a foreword by Glen Dawson.

11. *Hands Up; or, Twenty Years of Detective Life in the Mountains and on the Plains:* Reminiscences by General D. J. Cook, Superintendent of the Rocky Mountain Detective Association. With an introduction by Everett L. DeGolyer, Jr.

12. Will Hale. *Twenty-four Years a Cowboy and Ranchman in Southern Texas and Old Mexico.* With an introduction by A. M. Gibson.

13. Gen. James S. Brisbin, U.S.A. *The Beef Bonanza; or, How to Get Rich on the Plains.* With a foreword by Gilbert C. Fite.

14. Isabella L. Bird. *A Lady's Life in the Rocky Mountains.* With an introduction by Daniel J. Boorstin.

15. W. T. Hamilton. *My Sixty Years on the Plains.* With an introduction by Donald J. Berthrong.

16. *The Life of John Wesley Hardin, As Written by Himself.* With an introduction by Robert G. McCubbin.

17. Elizabeth Bacon Custer. *"Boots and Saddles"; or, Life in Dakota with General Custer.* With an introduction by Jane R. Stewart.

119

18. John F. Finerty. *War-Path and Bivouac; or, the Conquest of the Sioux*. With an introduction by Oliver Knight.

19. Frederic Remington. *Pony Tracks*. With an introduction by J. Frank Dobie.

20. Thomas Edgar Crawford. *The West of the Texas Kid*. Edited and with an introduction by Jeff C. Dykes.

21. Frank Collinson. *Life in the Saddle*. Edited and arranged by Mary Whatley Clarke. With drawings by Harold D. Bugbee.

22. *Fifty Years on the Trail: A True Story of Western Life*. The adventures of John Young Nelson as described to Harrington O'Reilly.

23. Edward Bonney. *The Banditti of the Prairies: A Tale of the Mississippi Valley*. With an introduction by Philip D. Jordan.

24. Walter Baron von Richthofen. *Cattle-Raising on the Plains of North America*. With an introduction by Edward Everett Dale.

UNIVERSITY OF OKLAHOMA PRESS

NORMAN